*Faith and the
Physical World:
A Comprehensive View*

Faith and the Physical World: A Comprehensive View

by

DAVID L. DYE, PH.D.

WILLIAM B. EERDMANS PUBLISHING COMPANY
GRAND RAPIDS, MICHIGAN

Grateful acknowledgment is given to the following publishers to quote from their copyrighted works that here accompany their names:

George Allen & Unwin: *Psychology, Psychotherapy, and Evangelicalism* and *Nervous Disorders and Religion*, both by J. G. McKenzie;

American Association for the Advancement of Science: "Tomonaga, Schwinger & Feynman — Awarded Nobel Prize for Physics," by Freeman Dyson, in *Science*, Vol. 150, pp. 588-589, 29 October 1965;

American Schools of Oriental Research: *The Biblical Archaeologist Reader*, edited by G. Ernest Wright *et al.*;

Doubleday & Company: "The Textual Criticism of the Old Testament" by Harry M. Orlinsky, from the book, *The Bible and the Ancient Near East* edited by G. Ernest Wright. Copyright © 1961 by The Biblical Colloquium. Reprinted by permission of the publisher, Doubleday & Company, Inc.;

Harper & Row: *Weymouth's New Testament in Modern Speech*, by Richard Francis Weymouth. Special arrangement with James Clarke & Company Ltd. Reprinted by permission of Harper & Row, Publishers; and *Christian Life and the Unconscious*, by Ernest R. White;

Inter-Varsity Fellowship (London): *Modern Discovery and the Bible*, by Rendle Short; and *I Believe in God . . . ,* by K. Runia;

Inter-Varsity Press (Chicago): *I Believe in God . . . ,* by K. Runia;

The Macmillan Company: *Miracles*, by C. S. Lewis, copyright © 1947; *Letters to Young Churches*, by J. B. Phillips, copyright © 1947, 1957; *The New Testament in Modern English*, by J. B. Phillips, copyright © 1958;

McGraw-Hill Book Company: *The Nature of Physical Reality*, by Henry Margenau. Copyright © 1950 by McGraw-Hill Book Company. Used by permission of McGraw-Hill Book Company;

Oxford University Press: *Mathematics in Western Culture*, by Morris Kline;

The Society of the Sigma XI for the Encouragement of Research in Science: "The Search for Meaning," by Joseph Royce, in *American Scientist*, Vol. 47, p. 534, December 1959;

The University of Chicago Press: "Procedures of Empirical Science," by V. F. Lenzen, in *International Encyclopedia of Unified Science*, Vol. I, pp. 281, 283, 285. Copyright © 1955 under the International Copyright Union.

Dedication

To my wife and family, who patiently let me disappear into my office for so many long hours to write; and to the many college students, discussions with whom have helped formulate these ideas, perhaps especially to Peter S. Fleming (killed by the Aucas in Ecuador in 1956) who was immensely helpful to me during my graduate school days when I was in the throes of appraising my faith.

Contents

7

I: *Introduction*

A. SCIENCE AND RELIGION

Science is a means of knowledge about the world in which we live. It is the best means of knowing thus far devised by men, as may be seen by tracing the history of man's understanding from ancient days through the post-medieval developments of science to the increasingly accurate descriptions of the universe available today. Only since the development of systematized knowledge of his environment has man been able effectively to harness for his welfare many previously untamed forces in that environment. Technologies based on scientific understanding have influenced nearly all aspects of Western culture, if not of all cultures, to such an extent that it is trite, although strictly inaccurate, to call ours a "scientific age."

The development of science as the best means of knowing about our world has precipitated many discussions as to the validity of any other means of knowing. Religions provided the ancients with most of their understanding of the world. It does not matter that this may not be a justifiable function of religion from the modern point of view. The historical fact is that as scientific knowledge has grown, the tensions between scientists and the contemporary religionists have

11

increased, with ground almost always lost by the religious traditionalists. A philosophical assertion widely held until recently is that science can elucidate and solve *all* of mankind's problems. In this view religion is almost entirely outmoded, due to some supposed inherent incompatibility between science and religion.

Reactions against this kind of "scientism" have been expressed by some of the foremost scientists and philosophers of the day.[1] What is now becoming realized is that man's needs are more basic than the types of problems science can solve. We need ethical guidance for life which the increasingly accurate scientific descriptions do not contain. Indeed, we need more than standards to guide our behavior; at a deeper level we need the goals in life that can provide the desire and ability to live according to those standards. The subtle trap into which many have fallen is to think that science implies some unique philosophy containing life-goals and ethical guides. The humanists particularly enjoy labelling themselves and their viewpoint "scientific." However, as we shall see, since science describes observable physical phenomena it can equally well support any philosophical outlook that is rationally consistent with these observable phenomena. To borrow a mathematical phrase, science is philosophically indeterminate. One's goals and purposes in life, which are intertwined with one's world view, are therefore also not uniquely determinable by scientific means.

The continuing predicament of man, made urgent for modern man by nuclear weapon technology (and by the population explosion), is that his basic and natural need for purpose is not satisfied by technological means nor by

[1] See, for example: René Dubos, *Dreams of Reason* (1961); A. Einstein, *Out of My Later Years* (1950); A. Toynbee, *Reconsiderations* (1961), *Civilization on Trial* (1948); C. F. von Weizsäcker, *The World View of Physics* (1952); E. Schroedinger, *My View of the World* (1964); Elton Trueblood, *Predicament of Modern Man* (1944); C. S. Lewis, *Abolition of Man* (1947); Lecompte du Noüy, *Road to Reason* (1949); others may be listed in Chapter VII.

scientific knowledge. A potentially disastrous substitution of means for ends, together with the growing suspicion that science may not, after all, have even the means, has produced a general feeling of purposelessness among people — especially young people — and has led even farther away from any truly effective resolution of their individual and collective predicament. Science has been popularly credited with superseding religion; if now science fails us, then it is natural to conclude that life is meaningless, a tale told by an idiot, a grim irrational joke. If some of the more frenetic voices are to be believed, the next step is human oblivion, whether with bang or whimper.

The intrinsic inability of science to provide man's necessary moral goals need not lead to despair, nor signify an irrational reality. The obvious alternative is that science gives us at best only an incomplete picture of reality. Science is the best — perhaps the only — means of describing physical reality, but if another category of reality exists by which needed ethical standards are determined, or our moral natures are to be satisfied, then science might not be applicable to it. If, as many contemporary writers believe, life makes no real sense, perhaps it is because they have a view of life that is based on incomplete or incorrect premises. A fresh look might enable us to fit all our perceptions together more satisfyingly.

Our human situation may be like a flat jigsaw puzzle with some key pieces missing. The missing pieces will give better sense to the ones we have. The missing pieces in this case, though, belong to a third dimension, and are not amenable to the flat puzzle rules. When this fact is realized, even the flat pieces we have (scientific observations) make better sense. When the higher dimensional pieces we can gather are fitted in as well, a grander-than-imagined picture is obtained. In somewhat this vein, J. R. Royce concludes, ". . . the final putting together of the segments of life will always be a highly subjective and individual task. It is this personal search for overall meaning which is essentially religious and which cannot be scientized . . . Reality-as-a-whole demands a total approach. . . ."[2]

The view of this book is that science treats only the physical part of our total environment. The other part — let us call it the spiritual part and leave it undefined for now — is also necessary for the fully satisfactory human experience of life. In short, the way that restless men are seeking is the way of a rationally consistent religion.

B. NEED FOR A WORLD VIEW

Not only mankind in general, but organized Christianity in particular and, more specifically, the individual Christian, needs a comprehensive world view. Such a *Weltanschauung* provides both a purpose for living, and a means of harmonizing one's experiences within his total environment. That is, the Christian's world view not only should relate his faith to the contemporary culture in an ethically significant way, but also should formulate a meaningful metaphysical approach that can accommodate scientific data. Without this kind of comprehensive view, the Christian is likely to be always on the defensive, perhaps unwittingly, able only to react irrationally against new scientific data he cannot reconcile with his religious views. The church's reactions to Roger Bacon, Galileo Galilei, and Charles Darwin exemplify both the inadequacy and the disastrous consequences of a traditionalist world view that fails to allow for scientific data. On the other hand, with a healthy world view that honestly — eagerly, yet critically — accepts all data, the Christian possesses criteria by which to relate his faith to his culture.

Two opposite, but equally irrational, approaches to science are common in Protestantism today. The fundamentalist view tends to reject as "science falsely so-called" any new data or

[2] J. R. Royce, "The Search for Meaning," *American Scientist* (Sigma Xi quarterly), Vol. 47 (Dec. 1959), p. 534.

interpretations of data that cannot be directly fitted into its existing interpretation of the Bible. The liberal churchman tends to accept without question interpretations and opinions of scientists and philosophers, even though they occasion drastic revisions or dilutions in his religious views. Both of these extremes are unscientific in that they are uncritical.[3]

The fundamentalist approach reflects an inadequate understanding of the fullness of Christianity, and it results too often in overt antiscientific attitudes and anti-intellectual philosophy. A more flexible view of science within conservative evangelical churches will prepare believers not only for their encounters with alien views, but for a richer experience within their own views. One must remember that the Bible itself teaches that nature, too, is a part of God's revelation. Further, the fundamentalist in practice often neglects the fact that any meaningful relationship with God must involve his whole person. A whole personality has its intellectual side as well as its emotional and moral aspects. An adequate Christian world view must satisfy the personality need for rational integration, that is, it must be intellectually, as well as ethically, consistent. Intellectual honesty is not divorceable from morality. The intellect shares in true Christian experience even though, in the Christian view, it cannot of itself fathom spiritual matters. Failure to fit a significant Christian world view to the intellectual needs of the present age, and an almost paranoiac adherence to a type of party-line scholarship[4] on matters relating to scientific data, has

[3] See J. I. Packer, *Fundamentalism and the Word of God* (1958), for an excellent analysis.

[4] See B. Ramm, *The Christian View of Science and Scripture* (1954), for some good examples and an analysis of this bad practice. Ramm's book is highly recommended. By "party-line scholarship" we mean what Ramm calls the "hyper-orthodox" approach (p. 26), which would require a person who accepts the Bible as God's revelation automatically to deny specific scientific ideas — biological evolution, for example — and would bias all its scholarship toward bolstering the hyper-orthodox party line.

cost the conservative Christian position the satisfaction of supplying the basic philosophy sorely needed by our society.

Where the fundamentalist has clung to his own time-worn concepts of Biblical authority, and extrapolated them into science, the liberal Christian has tended to abandon all such authority. He would retain only those elements of historical faith which he feels can provide him with meaning within his current understanding of the world. This sounds reasonable enough, but in fact such an approach wallows in relativism. It asserts, in effect, that our present knowledge is an adequate basis for judgments concerning the validity or truth of Biblical principles. If any one lesson may be learned from history and from science, it is that current knowledge is invariably superseded by deeper understanding. Since we humans have much to learn yet, one has no consistent or satisfactory way to select the "correct" beliefs unless he accepts some authority beyond his own reason.

A crucial objection to Christianity, understandably raised by many contemporary scholars, stems from the general failure of Christians to develop or demonstrate an adequate and significant world view for our age. The inference has been widely drawn that no philosophical framework can be made that is both truly Christian and consistent with observed facts of science. It is a most damaging allegation, for it questions the fundamental validity of Christianity at the philosophical level, which necessarily underlies the behavioral and ethical levels. If it were a true inference that consistency is impossible or non-demonstrable in the basic skeleton of the Christian view, then the ethical muscles of the Church, too, must malfunction. However, to continue the anatomical analogy, there are other reasons besides skeletal deformation for muscular dysfunction. Un-Christlike behavior or beliefs among professing church members need not bespeak inherent inconsistency in the foundations of Christianity itself. The fact that some Christians of every age, and particularly this one, have failed to exhibit world views that are either philosophically or ethically consistent need not be interpreted to mean that no such comprehensive views are possible. That the church has frequently failed to show to the world a vital meaning for modern life is admitted and will be accounted for in due course here. That the failure is inherent in the Christian view is vigorously denied.

Our purpose here is to show how to develop a consistent, comprehensive world view and how to use it in interpreting data. Since it is a *Christian* world view, it deals significantly with man's relationship with God; it is truly Christian in acknowledging the divine authority of Jesus Christ. Since it is a *world* view, it attempts to account consistently for the data of the physical universe, i.e., the observable phenomena described by scientific methods. It does not compete with the valid application of these methods, but rather it uses them. Further, since it is a *comprehensive* world view, it is flexible enough to accommodate data yet to be discovered, without modification of its essential nature.

Since it is *a view* that is being developed here, it must provide for the human personality some satisfying ends, or objectives in life, by which all of one's experience may be harmonized. That is, our world view should be both a means of making sense out of ourselves and our environment, and of providing goals, values, and the personality-transforming power to achieve these goals.

We make no claim that the view described here is the only possible one that satisfies these criteria. However, we shall attempt here to demonstrate the existence, if not the uniqueness, of a world view that: (1) is scientifically consistent, (2) is Christian, and (3) provides fully satisfactory meaning and goals for life. We present this view, briefly and generally, for examination by readers of every philosophical stripe. An intellectually honest modern person must sooner or later face up to the adequacy of his own world view. Specifically, a nonreligious person, scientist or layman, ought to consider carefully how much of the fullness of life he is excluding by his irreligion. The Christian must come to grips with his attitude toward science; he ought to consider how much fullness of the intended Christian experience he is missing because of failure to incorporate elements of modern scientific thought into his world view. Thus, this book is intended for the noncomplacent person who suspects some inadequacy in his personal views: the non-Christian who is willing to consider truths other than those science can treat, and the Christian who is wondering if faith is sensible in the context of the modern world.

As the reader proceeds through this book, he will notice the style is often terse. Many technical topics are touched upon only briefly or in passing. It may well be desirable to do some supplementary reading to pick up the details of such topics as carbon-14 dating, red shift, Old Testament textual criticism and archaeology, etc. Many footnotes cite references where a start may be made for further study. We treat various selected topics in only enough detail to use them as illustrations or examples of the consistent approach to data one can make in the Christian world view.

II: *Physical Reality*

A. SCIENTIFIC METHOD

Reduced to its simplest terms the "scientific method" consists of: (1) observation, (2) generalization, and (3) verification by further observation. Let us briefly examine these three processes as they are practiced by working scientists before we consider their philosophical aspects.

1. *Observation*

In the so-called "exact" sciences, observation usually involves measurement, that is, a quantitative description of what happens to some physical system under specified conditions. In less developed and "inexact" sciences, and in some fields of historical or human sciences, the observation tends to be more qualitative, perhaps only a delineation of relationships. Some have remarked that the degree of quantitativeness in observation measures the maturity of a field of knowledge, since the development of science has historically involved a trend toward more exact measured data. At least it is true that in science, the way to knowledge is through measurement.

19

V. F. Lenzen[1] states,

> The problem of empirical science is the acquisition and systematization of knowledge concerning the things and phenomena experienced in observation.

This view, according to Professor Henry Margenau in a general criticism of positivism,[2] is too narrow to describe the whole problem of science but is correct as far as it goes. It shows the need for observation in science.

The objects of interest to science are those things that are perceived by experience. The assumption that such objects exist is, according to Lenzen,

> confirmed by the reproduction of perceptions of them . . . The concept of the objective thing is social . . . [in that] . . . the scientific criterion of objectivity ultimately rests on the possibility of occurrence of predicted perceptions to a society of observers.[3]

In other words, a thing or a property of a thing (such as its position), has what we call objective existence if a number of people can make the same observation of it.

Observations, however, even if made by a number of different observers, need to be put into context in order to have meaning.

> . . . Significant experimentation requires the guidance of hypotheses which serve to predict and guide the results of observation. . . .[4]

[1] V. F. Lenzen, "Procedures in Empirical Science," *International Encyclopedia of Unified Science*, Vol. I (1955), pp. 280-339, a positivist philosophy apologetic. This encyclopedia contains many philosophical assertions as well as some interesting information about scientific methods. (The reader should, as always, distinguish data from their interpretation.)

[2] H. Margenau, *The Nature of Physical Reality* (1950), p. 18. See also A. Plantinga, "Analytic Philosophy and Christianity," *Christianity Today*, Oct. 25, 1963, p. 17; and for a discussion of positivism, Huston Smith, "The Revolution in Western Thought," *Saturday Evening Post*, August 26, 1961, p. 28.

[3] Lenzen, *op. cit.*, p. 285.

[4] *Ibid.*, p. 283.

The bare observation that a pointer on an electrical meter indicates some particular value, for example, has no significance of itself. It is what we might call a "raw" datum. If this meter is wired into some experimental apparatus we might use the presumably known theories of operation of that apparatus to assist in assigning some meaning to the meter reading. In other experimental equipment, the same meter reading would mean, or represent, something quite different. For example, in a particular laboratory apparatus containing some sensitive radiation detectors, such a meter reading might be arranged to be proportional to the number of radioactive carbon-14 beta particles coming from some material.[5] To interpret this raw datum (the actual meter-pointer deflection) in terms of the number of decaying carbon-14 nuclei, however, involves considerable data processing, taking advantage of many theoretical notions. In this example, one might further process the interpreted datum (a C-14 decay rate) using other presumably known cosmic ray and nuclear data to assign an archaeological age to the material specimen. In some such fashion, all the observations of science begin as "raw" data and undergo processing into interpretations, i.e., meaningful, related data.

Notice that there is a chain of interpretation between any observed raw datum and the meanings we may assign to it. Failure to distinguish raw from interpreted data leads many people astray, both scientists and nonscientists. It is tempting

[5] Carbon-14 is a radioactive type (isotope) of carbon generated in minute quantities by cosmic ray interactions with nitrogen in the atmosphere. This carbon finds its way into all living matter. Using radiation detectors we can determine the amount of carbon-14 present in a sample of material and, because of the known rate at which carbon-14 decays with time (half-life about 5500 years) and the (assumed) known generation rates due to cosmic rays, the amount of carbon-14 can be interpreted in terms of the time since the matter sample ceased to be alive, i.e., ceased to take up carbon-14 in its metabolism. This technique is one of a series of "radioactivity dating" methods commonly in use in archaeology (W. F. Libby, *Radiocarbon Dating* [1955]).

to think of an interpretation as though it were an observation. It is a temptation to be assiduously avoided by a clear-thinking person. The observed data of physical reality are objective, whereas interpretations need not be. The observed data are our basis for our description of reality. Observation is thus the process of our interaction with the physically real world whereby we may catalog occurrences of events and properties of things. Interpretation is the process of correlating these occurrences and properties into meaningful patterns.

2. *Generalization*

The interpretation of experimental data requires various definitions, assumptions, working hypotheses, and scientific principles — presumably principles that have been shown previously to lend consistency to data interpretation, and are accepted by a community of scientists. Thus we are led to consider the means of interpreting data, i.e., of assigning meaning to observation. This process may be called "generalization," since it is an attempt to gain a general or broad understanding of the relations between observed phenomena. Two approaches, called "induction" and "deduction," are commonly used to proceed from acquired data to the desired systematization of knowledge.

Induction is the process of generalizing from particulars. Its methods are classification of data, comparison of data, and correlation of data by quantitative statistical means. It is beyond the scope of this book to discuss it in detail.[6] Suffice it to say that what we find by induction is a "correlation coefficient," or the degree of probability of some relationship between sets of observed data. The relationship between the observed data may be involved or subtle, and not necessarily

[6] See G. Polya, *Mathematics and Plausible Reasoning* (1954), Vol. I, for a readable and full discussion.

cause-and-effect; all we know is that these observed phenomena are somehow related.[7]

Deductive generalization aims to explain observations by means of descriptions of basic mechanisms or processes in nature. Relationships between data that are only suspected by induction may be more clearly elicited by deduction. The process usually entails some working assumptions about nature which provide the basis for theoretical, purely logical, structures that describe how the observations came about.

The deductive or theoretical methods of science are the means of understanding why nature behaves as it does. By this question "why," we mean "by what basic underlying mechanisms" does such a phenomenon arise? For example, theories of atomic structure explain many observed data, including liquefaction of gases and freezing of liquids, electrical conduction properties of metals and insulation properties of nonmetals, and the specific colors of light from neon (or other gas-filled) discharge tubes, to name only three areas of study. Atomic theory is based on the working assumption that all matter is composed of many tiny building blocks called atoms. No one has seen an atom in the same way he sees larger objects, but so many diverse observations have been explained in terms of atomic theory that we feel justified in assuming their existence, and in inferring from the data many properties of atoms and the forces acting between them. What we are doing is describing the constitution of matter in basic terms. On this basis, using the symbolic language of mathematics, we explore the logical consequences of our assumptions. That is, we develop a theory. We find relationships that ought to exist between various observable entities, if the assumptions and theory are correct. In short,

[7] A striking example of how commonly used statistical correlation methods can fool one is given by LaMont C. Cole, "Biological Clock in the Unicorn," *Science*, Vol. 125 (1957), p. 874. No implication is made that these inductive methods are invalid; only that they must be used with care.

the theory describes the fundamental processes operating in nature that lead to observed phenomena.

In explaining these basic mechanisms, the theory derives and accounts for data. In fact, *theory must always guide in data interpretation.* Only if some pertinent thought structure exists can data be related to each other, that is, interpreted or assigned meaning.

Questions regarding the basic structure of nature are asked in most fields of study. As a rule, the tendency in science is from the inductive methods toward the theoretical approach as the field of study develops. For example, consider cell genetics, a field in which the first experiments were purely correlational (Mendel's peas, etc.). Considerable classifiable data were acquired on how cells divide and yet retain their properties. It was shown that the nuclei somehow control the cells' characteristics. Hereditary factors, now called genes, were shown, largely by inductive techniques, to be operative. Theories lately have been deduced and reasonably well confirmed, based on biochemical principles and cell chemistry data, that purport to describe mechanisms by which genes reproduce themselves during cell division. Such theory is based not on genetics *per se,* nor on a collection of correlated genetic data, but on biochemistry; yet it accounts for gene replication, and even suggests mechanisms by which virus particles attack certain cells, and other not-obviously-related cellular processes having medical implications.

The thought structures we erect to help us in understanding natural phenomena are not always correct. It is one function of these generalizations to predict data by which to check consistency. Often several different theories will account for the same previous data, but might predict different results for a new experiment. This situation then provides a means of testing hypotheses. Aspects of a theory which don't fit the facts may be discarded or patched up. New theories arise, and new experiments are performed. This is the way of science: generalization and experimentation interplay in developing more comprehensive descriptions of the basic mechanisms of natural phenomena.[8]

This interplay of observation and generalization illuminates the earlier remark, that data have meaning only within the context of a theory which correlates a particular datum with others. A different theory might interpret the same datum much differently in terms of a different underlying mechanism. As we try to describe (and in this way to understand) nature by the use of scientific methods, we find that theories are not always uniquely determined by the observed data.

In short, *an* explanation is not necessarily *the* explanation of given data. This almost obvious fact is too often overlooked by people and leads to dogmatism in data interpretation. As scientists, we believe that more data will serve to narrow the possible range of interpretation of existing data, and thus ultimately lead to correct descriptions of physical reality.

3. Verification

The power of the scientific method as a means of understanding physical reality is in its ability to correct itself through the interplay of theory and experiment. Inductive generalizations point the way to possibly sensible relations. Deductive generalizations describe underlying mechanisms that could account for the observed data relationships, and imply other relationships. The data, however, need the context of the theory to provide the means to interrelate data, and the possibility for data to be either consistent or inconsistent. Data are useless unless descriptions are developed in terms of which they become interpretable.

[8] An interesting account of this interplay in contemporary nuclear physics is given by E. M. Hafner and S. Presswood, "Strong Inference and Weak Interactions," *Science*, Vol. 149 (July 30, 1965), pp. 503-510. Another interesting and readable example of the process of development of a theory is E. Mendoza, "A Sketch for a History of the Kinetic Theory of Gases," *Physics Today*, March, 1961, p. 36.

The process of scientific verification involves acquisition of data that relate in a predictable or implicit way to some generalization. Simply, the theory predicts some result and we perform experiments to see if that prediction is valid. Within the context of the original theory, and/or that of the instrumental techniques, we can make a sensible interpretation of the new data. Either it fits or not; or, more likely, it partly fits the predictions. This turn of events leads us to modify the hypothesis and to repeat the process, to continue the theory-experiment interplay. When data begin to fit into consistent descriptive explanations, we are tempted to conclude that we are on the verge of proof of a theory, that we are discovering a scientific law.

B. CONSISTENCY, PROOF AND TRUTH

1. *Logical Truth — Internal Consistency*

At this point it is well to consider the nature of a "proof" in science. In high school we studied Euclid's proofs of geometrical theorems. First we assumed some definitions and some rules of thought, axioms, such as "a straight line can be drawn between two points." Then there were postulates, assumptions relating specifically to plane figures, such as "parallel lines never meet." With these ground rules we played the game of geometry, "proving" a theorem before we used it in another proof; and hopefully developing logical habits of thought.

These ground rules were accepted as presumed, unassailable, and obviously true, and no attempt was made to prove them. For, as Aristotle points out:

> It is not everything that can be proved, otherwise the chain of proof would be endless. You must begin somewhere, and you start with things admitted but undemonstrable . . . first principles common to all sciences. . . .[9]

[9] Quoted by Morris Kline, *Mathematics in Western Culture* (1953), p. 43.

Deductive reasoning always must be based on first principles — logical premises. Undefined but understood terms, and unprovable but accepted assertions, are the foundations of geometry. To define completely the terms of geometry would lead in circles, and would not serve to clarify the essential meaning of the terms "point," "line," etc. The axioms and postulates, on the other hand, appear actually to be logically unprovable.

Theorems are logical extensions of the postulates using the axiomatic rules of logic. One of the theorems of geometry we can prove is that "the shortest distance between two points is a straight line joining them." Although this may seem obvious, it is not too obvious to be proved, so it is a theorem rather than a postulate. But, is this theorem true? This question sounds strange, after we have belabored the obviousness of the theorem, but the answer helps us to see into the nature of scientific truth.

Is the shortest distance between two points a straight line? It is, under certain circumstances. It is not, under others. On the surface of a sphere it is not true; the shortest distance between San Francisco and Tokyo is a curved line, the "great circle." Euclid's plane geometry does not apply to figures on a curved surface. Suitable simple modifications to the postulates may be made, and a new type of geometry deduced — spherical geometry — which contains the theorem, "The shortest distance between two points is along the great circle passing through them." The point here is that these theorems are proved only within the framework of the assumptions made. If the assumptions are granted as true, then the theorem is true. Outside the framework of validity of the premises, the logical deductions need not be valid.

In the study of logic, the concepts "true" and "false" are not intuitive ideas of absolute or universal validity. A statement of logic is "true" if it is consistent within its framework of statements. If it contradicts, it is "false." The theorems of Euclid's "high school geometry" are true in a plane, because they are consistent there. A different framework is needed in curved spatial coordinates, and more general theorems are applicable (true) there.

In the late nineteenth century, geometries were developed which had postulates that were not only unprovable but also apparently inconceivable in simple terms. For instance, if we postulate that two parallel lines do meet, a "non-Euclidean geometry" can be formulated. Logical structures of this type may be consistent, i.e., no internal contraditions need exist. It might happen that no physically real situation exists (to our knowledge) to which this type of geometry applies, but that fact has nothing to do with its internal consistency. However, in this case, a four-dimensional non-Euclidean geometry was assumed by Einstein (in 1916) as a basis for development of general relativity theory.[10] It happens that many of the predictions of that generalization are observable. Many physicists and astronomers have accepted the broad outlines of this relativity theory as "true." This means that the theory and the experimental results are considered by those cosmologists to be consistent.[11] The simpler three-dimensional and the Euclidean types of geometry may be the ones which do not fit all the facts. They apply to small-scale happenings just as a sphere the size of the earth appears to be a plane to people as small and close to it as we usually are.

[10] In a four-dimensional space, time may be taken as the fourth dimension, along with the three mutually perpendicular spatial dimensions. To describe a point in such a space we need four numbers, say the distances along each of three directions from a preselected (and arbitrary) zero reference point, and the time interval from the chosen time-zero. In a curved space things are a little more difficult to conceive of, but there are well-written books for the layman on both special and general relativity with and without mathematics. See, for example, A. Einstein, *The Meaning of Relativity* (1950), or A. Einstein and L. Infeld, *The Evolution of Physics* (1938).

[11] Some schools of thought in physics still question the general relativity approach, and some experimental discrepancies do exist.

Although the simpler Euclidean theory of geometry is self-consistent, and has limited applicability, it does not agree with all the data we have about the universe. Perhaps a yet-to-be-developed logical construction will do an even better job of accounting for these physically observed data, and for data that are yet to be acquired.

The sum of this matter is that the scientific method can and does demonstrate consistency between generalizations and observations. A generalization itself ought to be internally consistent, i.e., logically noncontradictory. If, in addition, the phenomena predicted by the generalization are observed, then the generalization will have been shown to be consistent with observable physical reality, i.e., verified. This constitutes a proof, and this is as much as we can say. In science, "proof" is consistency; verification is external, i.e., observable, consistency.

2. *Scientific Truth — External Consistency*

The guidance supplied by this consistency requirement extends everywhere in science. If two similar experiments give different data, we examine both, perhaps perform them again, to harmonize them or find the error which we feel must have crept in. If two theories starting with identical assumptions disagree, we study the disparity to learn why. If a well-founded and reasonable theoretical prediction and a well-designed experiment disagree, we examine both the experiment and the theory to see if the observed data were properly interpreted, because we *feel* that they *ought* to be consistent.[12]

As scientists, if we can demonstrate consistency, i.e., agreement of our experimental results with theoretical descriptions, we say we have "proved" the theory. This is satisfactory; it is all that needs to be said. Absolute truth, if there be such

[12] Perhaps our feeling that consistency is a requirement stems from the nature of meaning itself. An inconsistent statement says nothing; it is meaningless. We humans crave to understand meanings, and so feel that there *ought* to be some ultimate consistency.

a thing,[13] is not to be found by scientific means; science cannot prove (or disprove) its existence by appealing to observation.[14] So, a definition of truth in science as consistency is an entirely adequate one.

Two further points must be made here. First, if some assumptions are made and a theoretical description of nature developed which predicts all the relevant observed data, we usually tend to believe in such assumptions more strongly; we would use them in other theoretical approaches. If further observations can be consistently interpreted in terms of these same theoretical assumptions, they acquire the status of scientific principle. In its history, however, science has abandoned many principles. It behooves us to remember that *in science consistency of data interpretations constitutes proof.* Principles, assumptions, and theories serve to organize these consistent interpretations of observed data.

Second, the need for a theory to interpret raw data, and the processes of experimental-theoretical interplay in the scientific convergence toward accurate descriptions also imply that interpretations are always tentative, since data are always incomplete. Another theory may better account for more data, as well as existing data. Freeman Dyson, of the Institute for Advanced Study, writing in praise of the 1965 Nobel Prize Winners in Physics, says of quantum electrodynamics, "The theory . . . describes only a part of physical reality, and it makes no claim to finality. But it seems sure to survive at least as a special limiting case, within any more comprehensive theory that may come later to supersede it."[15] This illus-

[13] The existence of absolutes is not in question here, only the limitation of science to prove or disprove them.

[14] Of course, if one begins with the assumption that observable nature is the only absolute that exists, then we might admit that he can make a self-consistent philosophy of science (naturalism), but we assert he has not "proved" the assumption by observation; he has merely assumed it for other reasons.

[15] *Science,* Vol. 150 (Oct. 29, 1965), p. 559.

trates the remark that proofs in science are tentative. Many other examples could also be stated.

C. ASSUMPTIONS

1. *Types of Assumptions*

Any systematic thought structure, of which science is an example, must have foundations. The validity of the foundations bears directly upon the validity of the structure. These foundations, and their validity, must be assumed. Such assumptions need not be blind or irrational, for by their very nature assumptions are not to be proved except by appeal to other, equivalent, assumptions. Aristotle's quoted remark is applicable: one has to start somewhere in his thinking. From the assumed basis, logical deductions may be made, understanding may be gained, and descriptions made in terms of the deduced structure.

We ought to distinguish two usages of the term "assumption" that will occur here and elsewhere in the literature of science and philosophy. In a description of some physical phenomenon, a researcher (experimentalist or theoretician) often will make a statement such as, "Let us *assume* that the equation for total energy of a system can be written in a certain form. . . ." This scientist then proceeds to work out the logical consequences of this hypothesis, and to investigate observed data in its light. There results a body of knowledge concerning the form of an energy equation. When the researcher made this assumption, he was just *supposing it in order to see what it meant*. The assumption in this case was a probe or tool to allow some insight into the specific nature of a certain physical system. To distinguish this use of the word, we may designate this a "hypothetical" or working assumption.

A different type of assumption, in fact, a separate concept, is the basic presupposition which may govern a way of thinking. We presuppose the validity of reason, thought — of the scientific method. Since it cannot be demonstrated, this assumption is of a more fundamental character than the hypothetical one made to study a particular phenomenon. This use of the word "assumption" may be designated "philosophical presupposition," to distinguish it from the other usage.

Now it is of interest briefly to consider the scientist's subjective relationship to his assumptions, for these two types of assumptions involve him in different ways. The scientist can (and should) be detached personally from the working hypotheses he may make in his research. These hypotheses are only on a "let's-try-it-and-see-what-happens" or a "suppose-for-the-moment-that-this-is-true" basis. Such an assumption is not, and should not become, an article of faith for a working scientist. On the other hand, the philosophical presupposition category of assumptions must involve the scientist deeply and personally. Notwithstanding some popular imagery, scientists are human beings and not automatons or computers. The whole character of a scientist's approach to understanding of nature is at stake in the presuppositions he makes. The scientist cannot help but *accept on faith* these presuppositions, or *assumptions concerning ultimate meanings.* They need not be believed blindly, since they make some sense to the particular person involved, that is, he can rationalize them. However, in the last analysis this type of philosophical assumption is simply to be believed.

It may be argued that the scientific method rests "not on faith but on experience," but note that we *assume* the reality of experience. We believe in the objective character of the reality that impinges on us, and we see things happen in a way that makes the scientific method a reasonable means of dealing with our perceptions. So we have demonstrated our faith in the scientific method by appealing to faith in more fundamental presuppositions concerning reality. These underlying notions are therefore equivalent, and are to be believed. They are the types of assumptions that matter to us deeply, for they have implications concerning deeper meanings, that is, meanings of nature that go beyond mere description.

However, notice that a philosophical presupposition is, strictly speaking, *ascientific*. It need not enter into the modes of interpretation used to process observed data. Indeed, it ought not. We arrive at data interpretations by means of truly scientific hypotheses, assumed for this very purpose of processing observed data into consistent descriptions. We arrive at philosophical interpretations of nature by invoking ascientific presuppositions. Distinguish the layers of meaning implicit in these two processes: (1) scientific meaning is descriptive; (2) philosophical meaning is "metascientific," deeper, and concerned with ultimate realities, or with the ultimate character of all things. The human mind, always probing deeper into the nature of its total environment, seeks some kind of underlying unity, i.e., metascientific meaning. This innate search for basic truth leads us to a personal involvement in our presuppositions that we normally would not have in the purely scientific inquiry for accurate descriptions of phenomena. Thus these presuppositions are a necessary part of our human make-up. They are articles of faith, for scientists as well as other men.

2. Specific Presuppositions Underlying Science

The three pillars of the scientific method — observation, generalization, and verification — rest on three fundamental presuppositions. These foundations are philosophical assumptions; they are widely, if tacitly, believed by practicing scientists. Consider them in turn.

The first part of the method, observation, depends on a fundamental philosophical assumption: *There is some reality to be observed.* When we declare we must observe facts in our scientific investigation, we are tacitly assuming that something we may call physical or observable really exists.

The second part of the method of science, generalization, leads us to another fundamental assumption: *Physical reality is of such a character that logic applies in its description,* i.e., nature is self-consistent; a rational approach is warranted and needed in our study of nature. What we call "logic," including mathematical reasoning, is applicable and adequate to the task of data processing.

The third part of the method of science, verification, leads us to a third assumption: *Some kind of causal laws applies in nature.* That is, there are principles by which one state of the universe is related to other (earlier and later) states of the universe. In order to be sensible about performing an experiment to test the value of some hypothesis, we need to believe that some kind of causal relationship exists between the different physical entities under investigation. It is in these terms that physical laws can be expected to hold as "laws," a given stimulus evokes a theoretically predictable and experimentally observable response.

These three presuppositions (in italics above) suffice to undergird and structure the whole scientific method. No further philosophical assumptions need be made by the working scientist in order that he may consistently believe in the validity and adequacy of science to describe nature. No less than acceptance of these three can give him the assurance that his scientific method functions. These three presuppositions are necessary and sufficient in order for science to provide descriptions of our physical universe.

Note that we do not need to specify any particular concept of physical reality, nor the formal properties of the applicable logic, nor the type of causality that operates. The particular meanings one assigns to these assumptions define, not his science, but his philosophy of science. Note also that science, based on these presuppositions, describes observable reality and that this is the proper domain and function of science. This is a crucial point in our world view, for by it we decide where the interface comes between science and philosophy. However, if science is to be the objective discipline most scientists consider it to be, it must be limited to descriptions of an objective observable reality. Questions concerning a scientific basis for ethics, the moral un-neutrality of science, or support for any world view, are valid only when understood as philosophical rather than scientific questions.

3. *Possible Meanings of the Presuppositions*

We humans, and perhaps especially we scientists, are not content with mere descriptions of nature. For this reason, we invariably add a few more presuppositions to the three we need for scientific description. An electronic computer may be programmed to receive experimental data, to process it by means of mathematical logic, and to predict results from another experiment — that is, to observe, generalize, and verify. Its working would depend only on the three presuppositions of descriptive science, and the output from this impersonal device can contain no conclusions concerning the meaning of the phenomena it describes, unless the human programmer builds these philosophical conclusions in at the outset.

There is nothing wrong with adding a few philosophical presuppositions to the three of science. It is both right and proper and, since all scientists are human beings rather than mere computers, it is a universal practice. The point of view implicit in these extrascientific metaphysical assumptions sets the philosophical course one charts in science. It becomes the means of assigning deeper meanings, i.e., explanations not purely descriptive, to what is learned by the scientific method. However, it is being intellectually dishonest to make these philosophical presuppositions tacitly, or to deny making them at all. Unrecognized hypothetical working assumptions cause trouble in scientific data processing, and unrecognized metaphysical assumptions likewise can lead one into unwarranted conclusions concerning ultimate meanings. It is very tempting, for example, tacitly to make some assumptions about the existence of God, then to place some philosophical interpretations on observed data. To claim that science then supports one's point of view about God is to forget that it was an *assumed* point of view in the first place. Yet many people, both atheists and theists, snare themselves in this trap of proving a premise. Insofar as it is intellectually dishonest, even if unwitting, it is harmful to the cause of understanding between schools of thought for any or all to hold unstated presuppositions.

With that introduction, let us now assign some specific meanings to the three presuppositions of descriptive science that will not vitiate their foundational character, but which will lead us to a philosophical position.

(a) Applicability of Logic

While the application of logic in scientific methods takes many forms, the most ubiquitous is mathematics. Mathematicians spend their time developing new logical connections between well-defined terms using axioms (rules of thought) and theorems (logically necessary consequences). The scientist's interest in mathematics originates in his presupposition that reality is logical, hence that mathematical logic applies to physically real situations. He uses this type of logic to assist in formulating consistent generalizations.

For the scientist, mathematics is a language of logic, the point of view developed in Russell and Whitehead's monumental *Principia Mathematica*. A succinct summary of some other schools of modern mathematical thought is given by Wilder.[16] Briefly, it is a matter of opinion among pure mathematicians as to whether mathematics is an extension of logic, other points of view being: (1) intuitionism, in which numbers and methods of operating with numbers are considered intuitive; (2) formalism, as described by Hilbert, a combination of axiomatics and logic defining operational rules to assure mutual consistency.

[16] R. L. Wilder, *Foundations of Mathematics* (1952), p. 229. An introductory account is given by G. A. W. Boehme and the Editors of *Fortune*, *The New World of Mathematics* (1958).

Those of us who would appeal to mathematics as an ultimate in logical consistency need to realize that it, too, rests on unprovable assumptions, and allows diverse interpretations as to its inner meanings. Before leaving this point, we mention a celebrated theorem due to Gödel, the metamathematician (one who studies the structure and foundations of mathematical thought). Gödel's theorem, in its simplest terms, states that in an axiomatic and consistent mathematical system, there are statements, theorems, which are undecidable, i.e., not provable.[17] In other words, such a system is inherently incomplete, nor can it be patched up by adding axioms.

Fortunately, the scientist's practical use of mathematics is not impaired by Gödel's theorem, possibly for the simple reason that observations can guide that use. Scientists use mathematics by associating or identifying some physically "real" (observed) entity with a term in a symbolic logical statement, or equation. Other entities are likewise associated with terms in the equation and the logical consequences may then be studied by mathematics apart from the experiment. For example, in the famous equation

$$E = mc^2 \qquad\qquad (Eq.\ 1)$$

the term E is identified with total energy of a particle, m with the particle mass, and c with the velocity of light. Another equation of Einstein states

$$m = m_0 \div \sqrt{1 - v^2/c^2} \qquad\qquad (Eq.\ 2)$$

where m_0 is the mass of the particle at rest, and v is the velocity of the particle. By logical manipulation (substitution of m from Eq. 2 into Eq. 1) we can write

$$E = m_0 c^2 \div \sqrt{1 - v^2/c^2} \qquad\qquad (Eq.\ 3)$$

as the relationship between particle energy and velocity. This equation is verifiable by rather direct experimental observation.

[17] Wilder, *op. cit.*, p. 261; see also Nagle and Newman, *Gödel's Proof* (1960), and "Gödel's Theorem," *Scientific American*, June 1956, p. 11.

Many other, perhaps more illuminating, illustrations of this process might be cited,[18] to show how mathematics is used as a language of description: mathematical terms are identified with an appropriate corresponding physical entity, and the originally abstract equation then is taken (hypothetically) as a model which describes a real phenomenon in nature.

Note that logical consistency is a necessary but not a sufficient condition for a statement to be identified with physical reality. This is because the principal content we assume for an applicable form of logic is that it be *noncontradictory*, i.e., self-consistent.[19] In logic, truth is defined as consistency. One can make logically consistent statements that do not seem to apply to the real world of science, e.g., those of Euclidean geometry. (We do not even need to assume bi-valued logic, although to date no great use of multi-valued logic forms has been found possible in physics, so that most people still think in terms of a proposition's being either true or false, i.e., either consistent or contradictory, with no middle ground. However, if multi-valued logic is some day found useful in scientific description, its validity will have to be assumed, too, just as is now done for classical logic.)[20] Without this consistency principle, we are without a means of thinking about the reality in which we are immersed. As C. S. Lewis points out,

> All possible knowledge, then, depends on the validity of reasoning . . . Unless human reasoning is valid, no science can be true . . . A theory which explained everything else in the universe but which made it impossible to believe that

[18] The adoption of group theory, an abstract formal mathematical structure, as a means of description by quantum physics, is a good example. See, for a good discussion of how mathematical symbolism is employed in science, R. B. Lindsay and H. Margenau, *Foundations of Physics* (1936), Chapter 1.

[19] That is, we assume physical reality to be self-consistent.

[20] B. Rosser, "On the Many-Valued Logics," *American Journal of Physics*, Vol. 9 (1941), p. 207.

our thinking was valid . . . would have destroyed its own credentials.[21]

If we can explain our rationality, or our logical consistency, by means of purely irrational causes such as accidents of cerebral biochemistry, then we have no basis for the validity of our thoughts, our logic, or our science.[22]

From this we see that a totally irrational nature is an inconsistent concept. Such a view of nature was more widely held in the recent past than nowadays. This variety of naturalism would hold that all causes and effects (including rational thought) are a part of the totality of an irrational nature. It is seen, therefore, to be inherently contradictory, because it denies its own use of reason.

Notice that an irrational nature is a different concept from a statistical nature. The latter view will be treated in the next section in some detail since it is a currently common view, it is not necessarily inconsistent, and it has provided some philosophical meaning for modern atomic physics. The confusion in terms between the statistical view and the irrational view of nature has, unfortunately, led many to believe that modern physics lends support to atheism. Surely, an irrational nature would be consistent with an atheistic philosophy, but, as we have seen, it turns out to be inconsistent with itself. If and only if it be assumed that there is something outside of nature, a self-existent and absolute rationality, which guarantees the validity of rational thought, can we provide consistently for the use of logic by science. At this point, as we are discussing only the content of the scientific presuppositions (and not theological assumptions), we need not consider whether this absolute rationality is personal or impersonal.

[21] C. S. Lewis, *Miracles* (1947), p. 26.
[22] Nathaniel Micklein, *Faith and Reason* (1963), argues similarly that rational beings could not emerge from an irrational universe.

(b) Causality, Statistics, and Quantum Physics

The use of mathematics and the whole process of generalizing in science has another implication besides rational
consistency. By a generalization we mean a description of
nature based on some previous perception; we expect this
general description to apply to some further experiment as
well, that is, to predict other data to verify the theory. The
implied tacit presupposition here is that nature is uniform:
if an equation properly describes an actual phenomenon at
one place and time and under a given set of physical conditions, it will do so at other places and times for the same
conditions. If a theory of the phenomenon doesn't hold always and everywhere, it is an incomplete or incorrect description. The fact that our scientific descriptions are normally
incomplete (and continually developing) means that our
present theories may not universally hold. However, the fact
that we use regular mathematical formulations means that
we believe in the uniformity of ultimate physical reality, that
is, in some kind of regular causal connections between the
physical parameters in the equations.

Belief in the principle of cause and effect has been an
important notion in the history of science, giving sense to the
process of verifying theory by experiments. In the development of modern atomic physics, however, questions have
arisen both as to the meaning and validity of the causality
principle, and thus as to the nature of physical reality. At
this point, a clear distinction must be made between irrationality (absence of the principles of logic) and nonuniformity
(absence of causal connections) in nature. Irrationality leads
to inconsistency; nonuniformity leads to chaos; both concepts
are inadmissible since they contradict the foundations of
science. There are now strong reasons to accept the notion
that all descriptions of phenomena, i.e., all physical laws, must
be framed as probability statements. It may be that nature
behaves statistically according to the principles of chance.

But, as we shall see, a statistical nature may be a much different thing from a noncausal, nonuniform, or irrational nature.

By the term "causality," we usually mean that one state of a physical system (a cause) leads to the next state (an effect) in time. The classical "determinist" idea of causality is that a given state must lead uniquely to a subsequent state if all conditions are the same. Two billiard balls bounce off one another in a way completely determined by their initial velocities, directions, masses, coefficients of restitution and rolling friction, etc. Determinism was found to be a useful expression of the causality principle in classical (pre-atomic) physics.

With more refinements in techniques of scientific description, classical determinism, which seems to work for macroscopic (large scale) phenomena, was found apparently to break down in experiments on the atomic scale. When atomic particles collide in a series of experiments, even with the same initial conditions, the resulting directions and velocities are observed to differ from collision to collision, unlike the billiard balls' behavior. In this case, and often in atomic and nuclear physics, a specific cause or initial state leads to a group of possible effects or final states. What is observed is that there is a *distribution* of final states. The modern theory of atomic interactions predicts this observed behavior, and in doing so intimates a "statistical view" of nature, rather than the classical determinist view. We cannot predict the result of a single atomic collision, but only the behavior of a large number of such interactions.

Probably most readers are familiar with the high school or college chemistry course picture of an atom, with an (electrically positive) heavy nucleus in the center and some number of (electrically negative) light electrons whirling about it in elliptical or circular orbits. This model of the atom, suggested by Bohr in 1913, accounted for most of the spectroscopic data and chemical facts known at the time. By 1925, more precise data had rendered the details of the Bohr picture untenable, and two physicists (Schroedinger and Heisenberg)

brought forth two independent and highly mathematical
theories based on quite diverse assumptions, approaches, and
mathematical techniques, but both of which accounted beauti-
fully for the then known data. It was later shown that the two
theories were equivalent, although not obviously so.[23] Both
theories assert that it is *intrinsically impossible* to make an
accurate visual picture (such as that of Bohr) of an atom.
The branch of physics which is based on these two theories,
along with a third independent approach made by Dirac in
the early 30's, is called "quantum mechanics."

It turns out that by quantum mechanics we can predict
(calculate) the chance of finding an electron at a certain
position (in a given state) in an atom. If we perform an
experiment with a large number of such atoms, quantum
mechanics will predict what percentages of them will be
found in each possible state; it gives a probability distribution. But we cannot normally predict the outcome of an
experiment on a single electron. In technical language, we
can describe behavior of atomic systems only by means of
probability statements.

We may write equations which describe these systems, and
these equations involve both observable and physically unobservable terms. An example of an observable term is the
wave length (or color) of light emitted by an atom that is
somehow excited. An example of an unobservable term is the
"state function" for an electron in a system, $\Psi(x)$, the square
of which is taken to be the *probability* of finding an electron
at position x. While $\Psi(x)$ is only a mathematical expression,
and does not itself represent anything which is directly observable, this state (or "wave") function is the basic quantum mechanical description of the state of an atomic system.

[23] As an example of the way science corrects itself and moves on,
and of the need for people to accept scientific pronouncements with
some tentativity, note that the equivalence of the two early approaches
to quantum mechanics has recently been questioned by Dirac, *Physical
Review*, Vol. 139 (Aug. 9, 1965), pp. B 684-690.

By performing mathematical manipulations with it according to quantum mechanical recipes, observable quantities such as energy, momentum, and position may be calculated. The light energy emitted by an excited atom is the difference in energy between two states. By quantum mechanics we can calculate probabilities of observing these entities in a single atomic system, or the distributions of these entities observed in a large "statistical" number of such atomic systems.

Whereas the semiclassical Bohr picture of an atom implied that we could describe the behavior and position of an electron in its orbit, the new quantum wave mechanics does not allow us to speak meaningfully of an "orbit" but only of a "state" of the atom described by the mathematical state function $\Psi(x)$.

Further, the new wave mechanics denies the possibility of making a simultaneous measurement of sets of two quantities, e.g., position and momentum (velocity times mass). If the electron's position is measured accurately, we find that its velocity is disturbed by the measurement so that we can know nothing about what it was during the measurement. A less accurate position measurement causes less disturbance to the velocity determination. An accurate velocity measurement precludes any knowledge at all about position. This frustrating turn of events is summed up in the famous "Uncertainty Principle" of Heisenberg: the product of the uncertainties in two (canonically conjugate) observable quantities in any system is always larger than h, Planck's constant, of value about 10^{-27} (an exceedingly small number: 1 preceded by 26 zeros and a decimal point). The Uncertainty Principle is especially important in atomic physics since the quantities involved are so small, but it is thought to hold even in the larger familiar world, though unobserved because of measurement error. This principle of uncertainty has aroused much discussion among physicists and philosophers, for some take it to mean that nature is inherently fuzzy and indeterminate (Bohr school). Others consider it merely as an observational principle, that nature is really sharply defined but we can only take fuzzy pictures (Einstein school). Still others point out that, as far as scientific description is concerned, it makes no difference (Bridgman's operationalism).

In return for taking away from us the easy-to-envision, photographically describable, determinate picture of an atom we had in the old Bohr theory, quantum mechanics gives us the ability to account accurately for the detailed behavior of the observed quantities. The old theory could not pass muster on the experimental details of the relative intensities and exact wave lengths of the light emitted by atoms in various conditions, nor the way in which electrons appear to behave sometimes as particles of matter, and sometimes as waves. The new theory predicts and accounts for these observed results and many more. But the new theory does this in a *statistical* way, predicting average collective behavior rather than the behavior of any one electron or light wave. From the point of view of the experimenter, this is not a severe restriction since we normally observe collective behavior of a large number of atoms in any experiment. But for the layman philosopher the new theory offers no simple picture, only mathematical formulae. In classical or nonmathematical terms it is impossible to resolve the paradoxical behavior of electrons and light waves — electrons diffracting as though they were waves, light waves ejecting particles (photoelectrons) or scattering (Compton Process) as though they were discrete particles. The paradox is more than a semantic difficulty; it appears to be characteristic of physical reality on the atomic level.

These facts emerge from the present discussion: submicroscopic nature can be adequately described, so far as we now know, by statistical theories. We can predict the collective behavior of large numbers of atoms in terms of probability distributions. This approach provides no classical diagrammatic picture of an atom, and has been even interpreted by some to mean that nature — "ultimate reality" — is indeterminate or fuzzy.

Some people have felt that these developments in physics force them to a statistical view of nature. It does seem that the type of *description* needed in the physical world is probabilistic, rather than deterministic in the nineteenth-century sense. However, this is a far cry from the common assertion that modern physics supports indeterminism as a *philosophy*. Such a metaphysical view presupposes that everything that happens is the result, not of order or regularity in nature, but of purposeless, chaotic chance. The mathematical laws of science would amount to no more than convenient usable summaries of the average effect of disorderly occurrences. In this view, the universe and man in the universe are accidents. One logical conclusion of this view is that thought itself, and all logic, are accidents of statistical phenomena in the human brain. As we have seen, therefore, this strict indeterminist philosophy undermines itself as irrational.

If the statistical view implies irrationality and if this is the necessary and only meaning assignable to the facts at hand, then modern scientific philosophy is, indeed, on the horns of a dilemma.

> This statistical view and the deterministic view are unalterably opposed. Although they both agree on the existence and applicability of scientific laws, they differ widely on the interpretation of these facts. Determinism asserts that scientific laws are statements of the necessary, invariable, universal behaviour of natural objects. The statistical view regards laws as statements possessing merely a high degree of probability . . . .[24]

We do not agree that modern physics forces us to the type of statistical view that would deny uniformity or causality. It is of course a possible conclusion, but it is not without the difficulties we have mentioned. We consider it entirely consistent with all the facts to take a more moderate view of

[24] M. Kline, *op. cit.*, p. 386.

causality: to wit, *causality operates according to statistical laws.*

There need be no contradiction in terms here between the concept of "statistical," and the concept of "law." Nature, i.e., physical reality, is statistical in its microscopic behavior, at the level where discrete particles are involved. But the behavior follows the *laws* of probability, which are as good laws as any. In fact, they may turn out to be the only laws there are, but *the fact that they are laws means that there is some kind of order superimposed on the statistical chaos of the atomic level.*

We see no reason to abandon determinist concepts altogether, when by a redefinition of terms we can retain enough of them to satisfy our metaphysical needs for rationality. While we cannot observe atomic states themselves (the Ψ (x) functions), the states do evolve causally (in time), since in describing these states in terms of probability distributions we are using causal laws. The observed entities (derived from the unobservable states) may not appear to be related in a causal, deterministic way, as they were in nineteenth-century mechanics, but this fact need not trouble us. It merely means that the causal relationships between observable quantities are more subtle than pre-quantum physics had indicated. The fact that the probability for a macroscopic violation of one of Newton's laws is not zero, though exceedingly small, is overshadowed by the fact that *we can determine that probability by use of uniform laws.*

We propose a concept of causality that is statistical, but in which the regularity of statistical laws is recognized microscopically as well as in the collective behavior of atoms. In this way, we retain a type of causality, which is important to us as scientists to give sense to verification. We are able to retain enough deterministic content to avoid the implied philosophical dilemma of a totally irrational nature, along with enough statistical content to satisfy the experimentally verified features of modern quantum theory. Further, as humans, it is comforting to find, as a by-product of this "statistically-determined" interpretation of causality, that it is possible to make a further consistent assumption about purpose in the universe. If we desire to assume existence of some grand design as a means of understanding the universe, no valid reason comes from within these causality considerations of modern physics to preclude or obviate that teleological assumption.

(c) Existence of Physical Reality

We have seen that the structure of physical reality seems to be logical or consistent, and causal or regular. While we *assume* rather than prove these characteristics for physical reality, the fact is that they lead to general observational consistency. The up-to-now tacit assumption that physical reality objectively exists completes the trilogy of presupposition we require in science.

Although to give an acceptable and adequate definition of physical reality is a metaphysical rather than a scientific problem, nevertheless we have a deep-seated intuitive notion that at least there is such a thing. Further, we humans feel that reality should embody characteristics such as permanence, externality, logical consistency, uniformity or causal regularity, and should be subject to observation. By permanence and externality, we mean that reality is there, even though we observe it fleetingly; it does not depend for its existence upon our observation or thoughts about it. These notions are what place most people in the camp of philosophical realism whether they are aware of it or not. But these notions are actually intuitively acceptable assumptions, not uniquely provable nor necessarily made by all who ponder the problem. As we have seen earlier, we need not specify the detailed content of reality, we need only assume its existence, to practice science consistently.[25]

What of the philosophical idealist?[26] He does not assume the independent existence of reality. But he does assume some kind of existence for physical objects, at least during the process of observation. To deny such existence would be to preclude observation and thus to reduce science to speculation. The concept of objectivity has more than a semantic connection with the concept of the observable object. Regardless of one's philosophical label, and regardless of what one assumes about the self-existence of physical reality, the actual process of observation involves an interaction between observer and object. It is the presupposition that this object exists during the observation process that is fundamental to science.

In this book we will begin to supply our bare presupposition with realist meaning. We believe that our theoretical and experimental attempts to describe the physical universe by science have a real goal. This is unprovable, but it gives us a sense of purpose in the scientific quest. We acknowledge that the descriptions we make of phenomena are approximations. By successive approximation — the interplay of theory and experiment — we hope to converge toward the ultimate description of the objective physical reality. It is this ultimate physical reality which we assume partakes of externality, of regular order, of permanence, and of logical self-consistency. Our gropings in the physical reality in which we are

[25] Margenau, *op. cit.*, p. 12, says, "One can practice science without even committing himself as to reality, without even using the word *real;* indeed, as a rule, the less said about reality, the better the quality of the science."

[26] A quite readable account of the idealistic view and a discussion of the disparity between the idealism of Bohr and the realism of Einstein in the significance of quantum mechanics is given by R. J. Hall in *American Journal of Physics,* Vol. 33 (August, 1965), pp. 624-627.

immersed tend to confirm the assumption, but a proof of it would be circular.

Much more of interest can be said about concepts of reality, but we have explored the subject sufficiently for present purposes. We now turn to the main implication of this assumption.

Briefly, our assumption regarding an external physical reality is equivalent to the assertion that the scientific method, i.e., *science, deals exclusively in the realm of the physically observable*. We do not wish to belabor this point, but it cannot be emphasized too strongly to our culture where "science is a sacred cow," as one book title puts it.

By the nature of its methods and its goals, science may be articulate, if tentative, in its descriptions of that which is observable — physically real — but *it must be mute on other questions*. A materialist might ask what other questions would possibly exist, since in his assumed view, only observed nature is real. For him there is nothing else except physical reality. The only things he can observe objectively are so immediate that he rejects the possibility of nonobservable entities, or asserts their insignificance. But it is precisely because of this inherent intractability to observation that we must be careful not to be dogmatic in such assertions. Nonphysical (or extraphysical) realities *might exist* unamenable to the common historically developed methods of science. Scientists should be honest enough to be quiet, as scientists, on questions regarding nonphysical entities. As humans, they may believe one way or the other about such realities, but they cannot bring science to bear on them conclusively, either for proof or disproof. No *ex cathedra* pronouncements from scientists are valid on such topics, because science must, in our view, limit itself to statements verifiable by observation. Atheism, or any religious view, is not scientific, nor necessarily antiscientific, but rather *ascientific*. Since science is descriptive of physical reality, metascience — religion or philosophy — is scientifically neutral. Religious statements, insofar as they relate to inherently unobservable (by science) entities, such as remarks concerning the existence or nature of God, are [not even examples of undecidable assertions in the Gödel sense. These statements are] in a different system entirely, outside the limits of application of scientific method. Science has enough of its own problems of internal consistency and logical incompleteness (in the Gödel sense of "undecidable" as well as other senses) without having to make religious statements as well. Possibly some of the traditional windmill-tilting by both scientists and religionists results from the very human desire to set the other side's house in order, to the neglect of one's own problems.

4. Summary of a World View of Science

Three basic, independent, but unprovable assumptions underlie the practice of science, namely:

(1) Physical reality exists and is objectively observable.
(2) Logic applies in scientific descriptions of reality.
(3) Some causality operates in reality.

These three presuppositions are both necessary and sufficient for descriptive science. When we begin to detail the meanings of these assumptions we are, in effect, adding further premises that are philosophical rather than scientific.

We here choose to mean by the first presupposition that physical reality is permanent, external, and is the limit toward which scientific description intends to converge. We choose here to mean by the second assumption that the law of contradiction in logic applies, i.e., that physical reality is consistent. The correspondence between logic, or mathematics, and reality is made by association of terms of logic with observable entities in nature, or with entities (such as quantum mechanical wave functions) that constructively relate to observables.

We choose here to mean by the third assumption above that causal relationships exist between states of the universe, and that the relationships are such that reality is regular. At the present development of scientific description, it appears that these relationships are statistical. This means that the behavior of atomic particles is governed by the laws of probability, and thus all of physical reality is, in this sense, statistical. However, we do not mean that reality is irrational or irregular, and we deny that modern physics forces one to any such philosophical conclusion. The fact is that probability laws are *regular*. They are as good laws as any, and they do connect and determine the states of atoms in regular, if subtle, ways. We will call this view "statistical determinism."

The meanings we have sketched here for the basic presuppositions provide guidelines for a philosophy or world view of science. It is a view that can allow complete intellectual freedom in observable data interpretation. Thus it differs from "scientism" and naturalism since these opposing philosophical views deny the possibility of any reality not amenable directly to scientific observation. In doing so they deny to the human intellect and will the freedom to search for and find any positive meaning to life. The world view here sketched also differs fundamentally from analytic positivism which would make merely a semantic exercise out of existence. The view we present charters to scientific method the task of describing physical reality, of eliciting all the interconnections and regularities in objectively observable nature. Within its domain of observables science roams freely, able to give by successive approximation convergent, increasingly accurate, descriptions. At any time data are incomplete, so science makes no claim to finality in its description; the strongest claim that science may make is that its descriptions account for all known data consistently. This is what is meant by scientific proof.

Our view limits science to the description of observable physical reality. Science is silent with respect to any extraphysical realities. By thus circumscribing science, far from weakening it or minimizing its importance, we enhance its function by putting science into a definable relationship with philosophy. We allow science to retain full and free objectivity by refusing to dilute it with subjective philosophic opinion, or questions of ultimate meanings. Science tells us how things happen, not why. In this way the scientific method can provide us with the means of rational consistency, if not the ends or goals and meanings of our existence within our world view. This is the proper function of science.

Because of its presuppositions, science is philosophically neutral. As we have seen, this potentially allows scientific inquiry to proceed unfettered by personal philosophic bias. Parallel to this feature of our view we find another result: the human mind is free to pursue religious truths with the conviction that scientific description can complement them. That is, our quest for personal meaning proceeds unfettered by the limitations of science, rather using science as a means of consistency. Instead of an inherent conflict between scientific and personal views, we allow deliberately for the possible addition of teleological, extrascientific or extraphysical concepts to our world view. Specific concepts will be introduced and fitted into the fuller view in the next two chapters. To avoid getting ahead of our story, we only assert now that our definition of science, limiting it to descriptions of physical reality, provides (1) for the freest, fullest, and most objective scientific inquiry; and (2) for a complementary and significant philosophical or religious inquiry, by which to arrive at a comprehensive, consistent, and personally satisfactory world view.

III: *Christian Presuppositions*

So far we have established that the practice of science rests on three fundamental and unprovable assumptions, and these articles of faith are necessary and sufficient for the job of science. That job is to elicit accurate descriptions of observable physical reality. When we begin to consider the meaning of the universe and our own purposes in existence, we must add philosophical or metaphysical assumptions. We are free to choose whatever extrascientific presuppositions we wish, subject to the requirement that whatever world view we build upon our full set of assumptions should be a fully consistent one. This implies not only internal consistency, i.e., no logical contradictions, but also external consistency, i.e., the meanings man arrives at in life from his world view should allow him to rationalize his experiences (data) in the real world. Before suggesting further criteria for the adequacy of a world view, let us state and discuss the Christian's basic presuppositions. Then we shall have the full set of assumptions we need for a consistent Christian position.

A. EXISTENCE AND NATURE OF GOD

1. *The Basic Assumption*

The basic presupposition of any religious view is that there is a God; belief concerning the nature of God varies depending on the religion. As in most religious views, so in the Christian concept (to be detailed presently), God is a supreme spiritual Being, inherently and necessarily unamenable to direct physical experimentation. One should not ask for a direct physical "proof" of God any more than he should ask for an *a priori* proof of the validity of logic.[1] However, as we have seen in the scientific fields, proofs are actually consistency checks based on the presuppositions. This same concept of proof may be thought of as a pragmatic (*a posteriori*) means of justifying the Christian's assumption. *We theists feel we can make the most satisfactory interpretation of our total data context by means of the assumption that God exists.*

No inconsistency arises between the new assumption and the previous three. This is not to say that just any arbitrary system we might erect upon the four axioms will necessarily be "true," i.e., either internally or externally consistent. If the system which we develop were to predict a flat earth, resting on the back of an elephant, then available physical data (e.g., from a reconnaissance satellite) shows this particular system to be incorrect. However, if we add to our earlier three general assumptions a further general assumption that God exists, then we obtain a set of four consistent axioms. If these four are to lead to truth, then we must build on them a structure which can be fully consistent.

The four basic assumptions of a religious scientist so far mentioned allow him to hold a *comprehensive* world view, that is, a way of thinking about *all* his perceptions. From what has already been said, we see that this comprehensive view should not lead one to be highly opinionated or contentious. Tentativeness regarding data interpretations precludes immutable dogmatism. However, the assumption that

---

[1] See E. J. Carnell, *Introduction to Christian Apologetics* (1948), Chap. IX, X, p. 159. "Proof for God is parallel to proof for logic"; without postulating some absolute rationality we cannot trust logic and therefore cannot use it to demonstrate (or deny) God.

God exists, as made by the Christian, does lead to the conclusion that absolute truth also exists: it is the all-inclusive meaning of all things from God's own absolute viewpoint. Our human's eye view of the universe is an infinitesimal, but real, part of the total. The Christian's comprehensive world view thus claims as its domain more than the ultimate physical reality which is the province and objective of scientific description. The view relates us to our total environment — the external physical universe, the internal self, and the eternal Spirit. No assertion is made here that we finite beings ever achieve this full understanding of our total environment. We simply presuppose that such a totality exists, and that therefore such a view exists, if only in the mind of the assumed infinite, self-existent, omnipotent, omnipresent, and omniscient God.

2. *Data Accounted for by the Assumption*

Let us now consider an example of data that must be interpreted within the framework of whatever view a person decides to assume. We have chosen the theistic view, but must re-emphasize that with these data we are not smuggling in a proof of God. We believe that the Christian world view significantly and elegantly accounts for these data. However, in the last analysis the Christian view, as every view, is to be believed.

Consider the existence of laws in nature. As we have seen, the laws may be statistical, yet the fact is that there are natural laws. In all the esoteric symbolism of modern physics, wave functions and associated probabilities employed in descriptions of fundamental processes of nature, we find regularity. Even the laws of statistics are uniform mathematical principles. Morris Kline remarks:

> The question, whether determinism or the statistical view of nature is correct, is not an academic one. In a designed and orderly universe, life has meaning and purpose. Assurance of this design gives man courage and reason to live and to

build. It also reinforces his faith in a Supreme Being, for the strongest rational argument for the existence of God is the argument based on a designed universe. *A thinking, super-human providence of a Grand Designer is almost a necessary antecedent of a mathematically guided natural world.* (Italics ours). . . . On the other hand if the statistical view of nature is correct, the physical world and man's role in it are irrational. Occurrences obviously serve no purpose and lead nowhere since they are merely accidental chance happenings. . . . Life offers nothing but the meaningless pleasures and pains of the moment.[2]

Kline argues against the theistic position, but to do so he seems to have set up only two alternatives. Either one is a classical nineteenth-century determinist, or else one must hold that statistical laws are irrational. Modern physics certainly suggests that natural laws are microscopically statistical, but nowhere is there a hint that these laws are irrational; rather, they are statistical *laws*, and they connect states of observable systems in subtle but definite regular ways. Any inference from quantum mechanics that the physical world is irrational, much less man's role in it, is a *non sequitur*. It is an unwarranted philosophical extrapolation.

Of course, Professor Kline's world view must also account for the existence of natural laws in some way that he feels is consistent. We are not arguing in this book that other world views are necessarily inconsistent, but rather that the Christian view *is* consistent. He has chosen from his two alternatives a naturalistic, irrational statistical view of nature. We have chosen a third alternative, that of "statistical determinism," which seems to account equally well for the observable data of modern physics, including the existence of natural laws. However, the quotation just cited has special significance for us as theists because the author intended it to embarrass the theistic position. The sentence in italics (above) is a stronger assertion than we would care to justify

[2] M. Kline, *op. cit.*, p. 388.

here, but it is accepted gratefully. Since the statistical laws of nature are uniform mathematical principles guiding, however subtly, the universe, there is good observed consistency with the assumption of the existence of God. In other words, the simplest way to account for natural laws, the observed regularity in physical reality, is by assuming a Creator who has established these laws. It is interesting, but not precluding, evidence that these laws are expressed in the language of mathematical statistics. God presumably could have established a classical deterministic Newtonian universe, but He apparently didn't.

3. *The Idea of God*

To assume only that God exists opens up a spectrum of possibilities concerning His (or Its) nature, and how (if at all) we mortals should interact with God. To specify that we are assuming the Christian God will lead us to consider the revelation of God by Jesus Christ. As a prelude to those considerations, we may note some of the Judeao-Christian concepts of God, which supply particular meaning to the general assumption that God exists:

(1) God is Designer and Creator of all the physical universe, and Sustainer of all its natural laws of operation. He is not a part of His universe, but stands self-existent and independent of it. Thus He exists in a mode of being different from us who are a part of the material universe. He "inhabits eternity," not living from moment-to-moment in a time sequence, but rather He is outside of time.[3] He is "hyper-dimensional" in that all of our common four dimensions of space and time comprise a subspace of God's Being. All of time is "now" to Him; all of space is "here" to Him.

God, as sovereign Ruler, does interact within created physical reality, the observable universe, but He does so according

[3] C. S. Lewis, *Beyond Personality*, reprinted as a part of *Mere Christianity* (1952).

to what our human understanding calls natural laws. He is not limited thereby, for in His wisdom these laws are of His own devising and purposes. It is possible that God works through the statistical features of natural laws, as suggested by W. Pollard,[4] but this *modus operandi* is certainly not the only means God uses, nor likely the predominant one. As it is with the spirit, which, like the wind, goes where it will, so a full understanding of the divine interaction with the creation is beyond our finite comprehension.

(2) Omnipotence and omniscience are characteristics without which it is difficult to conceive of God at all. God has universal authority: He can do anything He wants, that is, anything consistent with His divine nature. He is sovereign in all matters physical and spiritual. Omniscience carries the idea of all knowledge and wisdom. It implies consciousness and personality, but these two terms as we humans can define them are shallow. In the Christian view, these concepts are anthropomorphic only because originally the consciousness and personality of man was patterned, as a finite-dimensional projection, after God's own.

(3) "God is a Spirit," meaning that He is nonphysical in essence. What this really symbolizes is a mystery, largely hid from us space-and-time-bound inhabitants of physical reality. It certainly means that our strictly natural concepts may be only coincidentally applicable to considerations about God. For example, we see evidences that God is regular, rational, and consistent; if He is Creator, as assumed, these concepts as we used them in physics are reflections of God's character. But we would be limiting God to our physically-oriented concepts of Him if we think of God's consistency, rationality, or orderliness as being defined in our terms. This human tendency to define God's attributes in human terms leads to the charge that "man creates gods in his image," an observable fact of social history. The Christian interpreta-

---

[4] W. G. Pollard, *Chance and Providence* (1958).

tion of this fact was just indicated: being finite projections of an infinite hyperdimensional superpersonality, in our efforts to comprehend the Creator we use the most applicable terms we know.

4. *The Character of the Assumption*

Note that God is not postulated as a means of explaining things not now understood by science, as many naively think, and as many — Christians and otherwise — have mistakenly supposed in their past arguments. As science marches on toward more accurate descriptions of the observable universe, neither the concept of God nor the place of God in the lives of men need diminish. In fact, the opposite may be true. If science and its basic assumptions are understood aright, then one can see also the basic Christian assumptions in a better light. Belief in God arises, humanly speaking, from the inherent human need for comprehending meaning and purpose in life, and this type of understanding is *qualitatively different* from that of science's descriptions. Increasing the amount and accuracy of scientific description does not of itself lead us to acquire meaning in life, nor to achieve moral values. Satisfaction of these human personality needs takes place in a different dimension. The basis for finding a purpose in life must be extrascientific, that is, it must involve some further philosophical presuppositions which can lead to meaning. The Christian's basic assumptions are of this type: God exists, and has revealed Himself to us, giving us some spiritual perspectives. Because of the essential qualitative differences between the underlying assumptions of science and Christianity, there is no intrinsic way either branch of understanding can force the other out of the picture.

B. REVELATION OF GOD IN CHRIST

We have thus far been considering what theologians call "general revelation," or the possibility of interpreting the existence of the physical universe in terms of a Creator-God.

Nature is general in that observation is the privilege and prerogative of every sentient person. Nature is revelation in that if a person makes a theistic presupposition he can interpret his observations consistently and begin to satisfy his innate human hunger for meaning in life.[5] Such a one comprehends the orderliness and rationality, as well as the vastness, of the universe to be characteristics of the Creator-God. A God who reveals Himself to this extent could consistently reveal Himself more fully. It is the Christian's second assumption that He did: *God has revealed Himself in the person of Jesus Christ.*

1. *The Biblical Record of Revelation*

We know what we know about Jesus Christ because men who knew Him personally wrote about Him. If, as the Christian assumes, Christ really was revealing God to mankind, what these men wrote was important because it was a part of God's method of revealing Himself. In short, the accounts of the life of Jesus were inspired. By this we mean that God guided the men who wrote in selecting events to record, in remembering details, in the actual writing of the words, and in the textual preservation and editing which may have been done later. No less care could be reasonably expected of God for the accurate transmittal of His revelation to man. To assume that God shows Himself in Jesus Christ, and then does not actively ensure that the teachings and actions of Jesus Christ are properly and correctly recorded for dissemination to people of other lands and times is to think of God as slovenly.[6]

Among the sayings of Jesus are references to what we call the Old Testament, the Law, Psalms, and Prophets. It is clear

---

[5] No implication is intended that an atheist or agnostic cannot make what is, for him, a consistent interpretation of his data. "The heavens declare the glory of God . . . ," but only to those whose presuppositions allow them to listen.

[6] The subject of inspiration is taken up later.

that Jesus considered these scriptures to be inspired in some sense of that word. Also among the sayings of Jesus are references to teachings that should come after His departure, and to the authority of His disciples to carry on His ministry. We believe it is reasonable to extrapolate from the actions and sayings of Jesus (Gospels) to the Old Testament and to the rest of the New Testament. Thus, the Christian's second assumption may be restated: *The Bible is the record of God's special revelation of Himself to men.*

There are bound to be conceptual problems in any consideration of divine revelation. This second assumption thus has different significance to people with different interpretations of the physical symbols of revelation. The problems result principally from the inherently subjective aspects of the revelatory process, that is, from the fact that the relevant observable and objective physical data, although philosophically neutral, evoke our subjective responses. This is not to say, as many modern theologians assert, that the revelation of God in Christ is rendered imperfect by our human inabilities to understand and accept it. The physical facts of Jesus' life are as objective as any historical data can be, and the Christian's assumption is that God showed Himself by means of these physical facts, along with other related real data recorded in the Bible. However, even though our subjective human response (or lack of it) alters neither the observable objective physical facts of revelation nor their assumed spiritual causes, yet God's purposes in revelation are served in eliciting this response. Therefore, there is a subjective side to revelation, leading to differences in interpreting such basic objective data as Jesus' recorded words. Differences exist between schools of nominally Christian theology as to how much emphasis should be placed on the subjective aspects of revelation, and as to whether it is reasonable to extrapolate from Christ as the Revealer of God to the assumption that the Bible is the record of that revelation. These differences are matters of theological or philosophical opinion rather than of observable data. They stem from the assumptions we all make in assigning meaning to facts, in this case from the assumed significance we as individuals place on the basic presuppositions that God exists and reveals Himself.[7]

We choose here to assume that God's revelation of Himself in Christ is recorded in its various aspects throughout the documents we know as the Bible. The written word is the vehicle for the Living Word. Specifically, *we postulate that Biblical statements comprise a data category for this Christian view*. Further, the statements themselves are objective data, being collections of words, i.e., semantic symbols. As data they are to be interpreted.

By way of justifying this meaning for the assumption, consider one alternative, namely, that among the Biblical narratives there are occasional scraps of real data that God would use to reveal Himself to us, and that we must ourselves decide whether or not God speaks to us through any given passage. While we would agree that God uses various Biblical passages at different times in our lives, it seems less than satisfactory to weaken the objective nature of God's revelation by requiring validation by the subjective response of a finite and (initially, at least) spiritually blind human. This feeling of dissatisfaction with an alternate view constitutes no proof that our view is valid, since no proof is possible for any assumption concerning validity. However, we again feel we can build an *a posteriori* argument to justify our faith in the revelatory character of the Bible. To wit, the Christian view we shall erect on this assumption allows us both external and internal consistency. It is not our purpose to prove any stronger assertion than that. A comprehensive consistent Christian world view will be shown possible, based

[7] We encourage further study in this rather complex theological aspect of faith, for example, in the writings of E. J. Carnell, J. I. Packer, Gordon H. Clark, Carl F. H. Henry, and Bernard Ramm, both in cited and other works of these authors; also in such journals as *Christianity Today, The Christian Graduate* (British IVF magazine), and *His* (U.S. IVCF magazine).

on the five presuppositions with the meanings we have presented and discussed. Thus we shall consider the statements of the Bible to be data in what follows, and investigate some of the consequences of this assumption. In this process it is important to recognize that even if we can rationalize a Christian faith by means of a consistent world view structure based on these assumptions, it is still faith; there is no way to avoid making and believing some basic assumptions in either science or religion.

2. *The God Christ Reveals*

The outstanding Biblical statement regarding God is that "God is Love." There is consistency between the general revelation in nature and the special revelation in Christ on this point, although nature emphasizes more the sovereignty and power of God, to wit, His deity. Yet the ability of man to be tender and compassionate — humane — can be interpreted as a reflection of God's own character. The existence of evil and pain in the universe need not be interpreted, as so many people are wont to do, as any lack in God's love. It is interpretable in the Christian view in terms of human rebellion against God's love, and the natural consequences of that rebellion.[8]

We should not restrict our concept of God as love personified by interpreting this revealed statement to mean only "God acts in love," or "God loves us," although these two meanings are taught in the Bible as part of that concept. The Christian idea of love is a giving of one's self, an ubiquitous notion in scripture, well exemplified in Jesus Christ. Love is an essential part of the character of God, and a study of this truth is one of the most rewarding analyses a

[8] As a starting point for further study of this problem, see C. S. Lewis, *The Problem of Pain* (1944). See also Carnell, *op. cit.*, Chap. XVI, XVII.

person can make, because of the enlarging effects on us of the deeper knowledge of God.

As a means of illustrating to us His love, we find in the Bible word pictures such as the phrase "Your Heavenly Father." The Creator known from nature is further revealed as a Father who cares for His children. We are able to grasp the idea of fatherhood from our natural experiences, and this illustration helps us to understand God's supernatural love. According to one passage in the Bible, the whole father-concept is derived from God's Fatherhood (Eph. 3:15).

The nature of love is to give itself, to share. The Biblical word "fellowship" pictures God's sharing of Himself; a person may have fellowship with God because God has shared His own special, divine quality of life with that one by virtue of what Jesus called the "new birth." Christ reveals God to us as One who desires fellowship with us, One whose love-nature causes Him to share His own life. A believer is a "partaker of the divine nature," and has the privilege of fellowship with God, freed by truth and walking in its light.

Along with the revelation of God as love, there is the Biblical revelation of God's justice, righteousness, and holiness. Thus tempered, the concept of God's love is not to be diluted into a maudlin, sentimental mockery of true love. The just Judge, the righteous Ruler, and the holy Father are all integral to Jesus' teachings.

Another aspect of God's character shown in the special Christian revelation is His interaction with His creation. God is not a far-off unapproachable impersonal force, nor merely the "Ground of Being," but a living Person. He is Life, and in interacting with us shares His unique quality of life. He is the Vine, we the branches. There is the aspect of the eternal God perceived by us mortals as a thirty-three-year period of time in history, during which God interacted with His creation to reveal Himself specially in the person of Jesus Christ. This is the central meaning of the second Christian assumption.

3. Parenthetical — The Supernatural

(a) Philosophical Consistency of Supernaturalism

While the Christian accepts a supernatural reality, many modern persons feel that they cannot do so. Our society, and science generally, ignores, denies, or ridicules the whole concept of the supernatural. This amounts to defining or assuming physically observable phenomena to be all that exist. An atheist should be careful he does this sentiently and not tacitly. As we have seen, no unequivocal observational proofs for or against the existence of God are possible. Further, one can make as strong a psychological accounting (in terms of wish-fulfillment) for why someone would believe in "scientific" atheism as for why one would accept supernatural Christianity, and neither accounting would be relevant to the validity of either view.[9]

If we deny real existence of nonobservables, that is, if we assume naturalism or atheism, we can have no implicit assurance that logic is applicable to reality. One must explicitly presuppose such assurance. It thus seems to many people easier to rationalize the basic assumptions of natural science if they also assume *something* — call it supernature or whatever — outside and beyond physical, observable nature. To assume such a supernature is not logically necessary, but it is philosophically satisfying. It provides us with some sense of guarantee that our whole human basis of thought about the observable world is not merely an accident of cerebral biochemistry. It consciously validates our use of reason, which an atheist or agnostic must accept blindly as valid. The assumption of the existence of God, of supernatural reality, is thus not inimical to the use of reason, but complementary and supporting. It provides meaning to the assumptions of pure science.

[9] R. E. D. Clark, in *Scientific Rationalism and the Christian Faith* (1945), makes an analysis of J. Huxley's and J. B. S. Haldane's dogmatic naturalism in terms of their childhood environments, among other things.

Along with the assurance that the observable world has
significance, and the scientific method is valid for describing
that world, the assumption of a supernature brings us to
consider how, if at all, it interacts with commonly observable
physical nature. At this point again one must assume, i.e.,
believe, something. And it is at this level of assumption that
the human person senses that he is going to become involved
and may develop an antisupernatural attitude as a means of
avoiding involvement. As we shall see, however, personal
involvement in some metaphysical belief is necessary for
human personality fulfillment. So it is not inconsistent for
the Christian to assume that the supernatural world involves
him personally, and that he may know of that other sphere
of reality because of what Jesus Christ has revealed.

(b) Miracles

In actuality, the basic problem the modern mind encounters in the supernatural is of the philosophical character
just outlined. That is, it is a matter of presuppositions. However, the way many modern people express this problem is
to object to miracles.[10] They argue that a consistent, causal,
uniform nature cannot countenance any capricious tamper-
ing from outside. Hence they claim they cannot accept
miracles or supernatural phenomena as real data. The trouble
with this argument is that it overstates the case. The Christian concept of miracles is not that God intervenes in nature
out of whimsy or caprice, as the ancients may have supposed. In the consistent Christian view, miracles are natural
consequences of the character of the God who both created
and interacts with nature. Among the revealed data is the
statement that all of God's works praise His name. Even our

[10] Aside from the trivial objection that the supernatural involves
Halloween-style ghosts and superstitions, an objection that any serious
student of Christian truth will easily see as a spurious "straw man";
see C. S. Lewis, *Miracles* (1947).

rebellion (as well as our saintliness) ultimately will serve the glory of God. Both the natural universe and the supernatural spirit world contribute to the eternal hymn.

When, in specific historical instances, the purposes of God are served by an event that is not understood, or is out of the ordinary, the observers have often called the event a "miracle." The extraordinary character of the event may have been its *coincidence* or timing with respect to other events. This is, in fact, the most common miracle, and is passed off as chance coincidence by the unbelieving world. Yet the Christian recognizes the loving hand of his Heavenly Father and glorifies God.

An observable but not understood event is hard for the observer himself to shrug off as spurious data, even though it lacks the repeatable, statistically controlled (objective) character often needed to convince another person. The fact that it was not understood was enough evidence for the pre-scientific mind to call it a miracle and ascribe it to a supernatural agency. Lightning bolts, earthquakes, or bubonic plague in the enemy camp were considered miracles because they were unexplainable. The modern Christian may consider these and many other Biblical events miraculous because of the timing involved. God's purposes were served in defending His good name against that of Baal, or in destroying a wicked city, or in winning a war for Judah, and He used what we now call natural events to accomplish His will. This is the criterion by which to define a miracle: *God's purposes are being specifically accomplished in a physical event.* That is, the miraculous element in some happening is not necessarily its extraordinariness, nor our inability to explain it in natural physical terms, but rather it is in the use God makes of the event to glorify His name.

There are some events described in the Bible for which we still have no scientific explanation, e.g., Elisha's floating axe, or Hezekiah's sundial, or the raising of Lazarus from the dead.

One can have his choice of interpretation of these data:[11] (1) there are scientific (i.e., phenomenological) explanations, which may be found some day; (2) God intervened in an unusually direct way; (3) the presently available recorded data are faulty in some respects, i.e., the originally revealed data have been textually corrupted. Simply because we assume that miracles are possible we gain no license to be gullible or sloppy in scholarship.

The one intervention of God in history that underlies all others is the Incarnation, or the "enfleshment" of the eternal God in the physical human body known temporally as Jesus Christ. It is primarily by this means that God reveals Himself. Any other event in which God interacted in history subserves that revelation. These other events — the miracles so commonly used as an excuse for disbelief — served God's purposes in showing Himself locally and as signs for certification of various messengers being used to reveal God's nature or will in specific ways.[12] The main event is the manifesting of God "fully," in the person of the "eternal Son" (phrases whose interpretation would take us far from the purpose of this book), an unveiling of glory that spiritually illuminates all the world and all of time.

C. A COMPREHENSIVE CHRISTIAN WORLD VIEW

The foundations are now laid, and a few pillars and beams in place, indicating the philosophical structure that can be erected. It is a world view that recognizes the existence of

[11] Ramm, op. cit., pp. 156ff.

[12] The raising of Lazarus to physical life — in fact all the "signs" recounted by John in his Gospel — is part of the demonstration that "Jesus is the Christ," that "God was in Christ." It is an example of a miracle for which no fully adequate scientific explanation has yet been given. When, as, and even if a complete descriptive understanding is obtained of the nature of physical life and death, we still have the miracle itself, the use God made of the event to show Himself in Christ.

spiritual reality and the position of Jesus Christ as the one who authoritatively mediates meaning and provides purposes for living spiritually significant lives. To the assumptions underlying the scientific method of description of the observable universe, we add the existence of God and explicit acceptance of the Biblical record as God's revelation to mankind. Thus a specifically Christian philosophy arises from these foundations. It is now our object to explore briefly both the internal and external consistency of this view.

1. *Physical and Spiritual Reality*

The implication of our five presuppositions is that general and special revelation are mutually consistent. In short, "all truth is God's truth." The facts of nature and the statements of scripture must together constitute a harmonious total structure of truth. That is, the raw data from both spheres of reality are to be interpreted jointly. The already processed data found in many scientific treatises are not reconcilable with the already processed data found in many theological books, simply because of the disparate philosophies underlying the data processing for the two extremes. This is the basis for the commonly observed arguments between some scientists and some religionists. The only intrinsic disagreement is philosophical and therefore is assumed. On the wider philosophical base we have given here, intrinsic agreement is assumed. A world view that accounts for all data is possible. Although we finite humans may never get the full picture, yet we have in effect assumed that such an ultimate total reality exists.

As subsets of the ultimate total reality, we have postulated the two spheres, physical and spiritual reality, about which we can know something, by scientific observation in the one case, by more specific revelation from God in the other. Spiritual reality is not particularly occult, ghostly, or science fictional; while it is qualitatively different from physical reality, it is certainly no less real in any meaningful sense of that word.[13] Jesus Christ taught the real existence — permanence, effectiveness, externality — of spiritual entities and relationships. These spiritual things are eternal, and in that sense at least are even more real than temporal physical realities. That they are not directly observable by scientific physical methods only points up the qualitative difference between the spiritually and physically real and the limitations of our physical senses. Perhaps, just as the frog's brain seems to be "programmed" to see only a moving and not a stationary fly, our senses are arranged to respond only to physically real stimuli.[14] Spiritual things are to be grasped only by faith, according to the revealed record. The faith thus spoken of is a vital personal recognition of God's authority that issues in willingness to become a part of God's purposes. "If anyone is willing to do God's will, he shall know. . ." Such is the epistemology of Christianity.[15]

2. World View Dynamics

Now consider the ways people build world views. We are continually bombarded with perceptions. The natural dynamic human need for consistency in outlook effects in us the development of some viewpoint even early in life to interpret these perceptions. Parents and culture guide in this. As we grow in both experience and knowledge of how other people have interpreted their data, we try to fit our new per-

[13] C. S. Lewis illustrates this in *The Great Divorce* by the blades of grass in heaven, which were so real that they cut the feet of one who had not acquired the same quality of reality by being made fit for heaven.

[14] According to Jerome Lettvin, of M.I.T., a frog will starve to death in the midst of food if the food does not move. This is traced to the ability of the eye and optic nerve to interpret visual stimuli before impulses are sent to the brain (*Proceedings of I. R. E.*, Nov. 1959, p. 1940).

[15] We take this theme up later, in Section IV C 4 (a), pp. 99ff.

ceptions into the primitive view and begin to develop a more mature philosophy, more adequate to its task. Its task, to provide a framework of meaning on which we may hang the data we constantly receive, involves all facets of our personalities to some extent. It is natural and easy to have emotional involvement in our own world view; indeed, it is impossible to be entirely objective, least of all about ourselves.

So people, including scientists and Christians, approach their respective data with philosophical preconceptions. The common processes leading to a world view are simplified and illustrated in Figure 1. The circle represents the raw data of observable reality and the box to the right both the interpretive process and the interpretations placed on these data. The world view one holds, shown as the right-hand box, is based on presupposition and receives interpretations as its input data. Figure 1 shows only physical reality assumed, so it illustrates the building of a materialist or naturalist view.

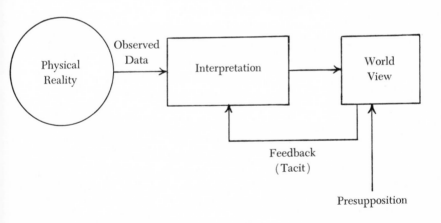

FIGURE 1. The Building of a Materialist World View

Raw data in science must be interpreted in terms of some theory. Insofar as they are purely scientific (descriptive) and not philosophical, the meanings assigned data may be checked for consistency by further appeal to observed data. However, because humans crave more than descriptive meaning, we often bring our philosophical assumptions into the interpretive process, and this is indicated by the arrow labelled "feedback" in the diagram. The world view may even influence the way data is taken, as we subconsciously try to bolster our position. What happens in practice is that we select the data or interpretation of data that best fits the meaning we *want* reality to have. Then some of us have the temerity to assert that one or another world view is "scientific" or "proved." It is clearly seen that such an argument is circular. One's view may be modified, developed, or rationalized, but insofar as it is not physical but metaphysical it is based on unprovable (although possibly consistent) presuppositions.

Christians, being human, widely fall into the same trap in interpreting the basic objective data of the statements of the Bible. The trap consists in failing to recognize and account for the feedback in the process. This failure leads invariably to dogmatism and unhealthy emotional involvement in one's own interpretations. In the case of the Christian it is tantamount to his equating his own interpretations with the scriptures themselves, a practice roundly condemned by Jesus Christ in the religious traditionalists of His day.

The feedback in the process is both necessary and normal, and nothing is wrong with it *per se*, for it allows one stability in viewpoint, and thus stability in personality. However, when the feedback is unrecognized as such we also forget how the same raw data might lead another person consistently (i.e., honestly) to different conclusions from our own. Tolerance is as important for the scientist as it is for the Christian. Tentativeness of all scientific conclusions, which is a truly scientific attitude, is analogous to humility. This attitude keeps the communication channels open to other views, even variant ones, and allows rational evaluation of one's own consistency as well as the other fellow's.

3. *Some Examples of Feedback*

Both scientists and religionists are guilty of closing their minds to unpopular views of their colleagues, in addition to being unwilling to hear each other's different philosophical approaches. A striking example in science is found in "The Piltdown Affair."[16] When, in 1915, several hominoid cranial bones were found near Piltdown in England, the prevailing scientific view in anthropology was that early man's brain development had led him up the evolutionary path. Some careful observers cautioned that the evidence was scanty. The Piltdown artifacts consisted of only a few pieces not obviously related, but the scientific community as a whole accepted "Piltdown man" as the earliest manlike ape with a large cranial capacity. Full reconstructions, including a hairy chest and a bone club, appeared in textbooks the world over. As more observed data accumulated, Piltdown man became an anomaly in the emerging pattern, and the artifacts were examined more closely. It was found that at least some of these bones were fraudulent, teeth having been artificially abraded and bone chemically treated to give an appearance of age. In this case, scientists had accepted almost without question data that had fitted their preconceived notions concerning the evolution of the human body, and pointed authoritatively to their processed data to refute any who did question. The power of the scientific method to elicit truth in physical reality finally showed itself and presumably a more accurate description emerged.

The case of Galileo is an example of the same kind of failure to recognize the feedback and maintain tentativeness among religionists. In the sixteenth century the Church,

[16] See W. L. Strauss, "The Great Piltdown Hoax," *Science*, Feb. 26, 1954, for the details of this case. We can only summarize here.

predominantly Roman in this case, held to Aristotelian and Ptolemaic physics, and had so rationalized their religious views of science. Galileo's audacity in experimenting with falling balls, pendulums, and telescopes was considered an affront to Christianity, because the Church's position on these matters was held to be final and absolute. A few Biblical statements were interpreted to mean a flat earth and a geocentric universe. There was no room for any more data, and a far-reaching controversy developed between Renaissance science and Christianity. The same Biblical statements formerly cited in support of these medieval views are now interpreted quite differently, and this particular field of science (astronomy) is readily harmonized within contemporary Christianity. Nowadays it is biological evolution (or cultural anthropology or Freudian psychology) that raises the hackles of many churchmen and the scornful eyebrows of many scientists.

We hope, in what follows, to sketch with a broad brush means of explaining observed data from these controversial fields within a comprehensive Christian view. Our purpose here has been to point out the need of all people to (1) be tentative and humble in forming conclusions, (2) distinguish raw from processed data, and (3) recognize presuppositions and the influence of one's world view on his data interpretations.

4. The Proposed Consistent World View

With that lengthy introduction, we can diagram a dynamically developing, comprehensive Christian world view in Figure 2. The circle represents the totality of reality, including the observable physical part and the spiritual part of which we may know some things because they are Biblically revealed. Scientific observation, the organizing of interpretation into descriptions, and verification by further appeal to data, are essentially as presented earlier. Analogously, Biblical statements are taken, interpreted, and the theological or practical interpretations checked for consistency by appeal to the scriptures again, e.g., by cross-reference study. The five presuppositions of our total view both allow and require scientific description and significant understanding of God's ways to fit together to form a consonant and integrated way of thinking. Mutual aid between the respective channels of interpretation ("crosstalk," to use the figure of speech of the electronic engineer) guides in the assignment of meanings both to scientific hypotheses and Biblical statements. Thus harmony results in the culminating viewpoint. As always with us humans, feedback exists, since the data and their interpretations would not lead uniquely to a philosophical position without some guidance from the presuppositions. If the presence and purpose of the feedback is recognized and understood, it provides for the mature stability needed in our personality development.

The diagram of Figure 2 shows observed data in physical reality being interpreted jointly with the objective statements of scripture. In addition to objective scientific data, the observed physical data may consist of religious experiences or feelings generated within the relationship between the believer and God by his faith. These subjective data might include events that happened after praying for them to happen, or the person's ability to resist a particular temptation to do wrong, or the inner joy that accompanies the experience of faith that one's sin has been forgiven by God, or other such religious data. These things are observable, although they may originate in or result from an interaction between the Spirit of God and the physical person. In this sense these data come from the sphere of spiritual reality into the interpretive process. The human person is partly physical — the body and its physiology — and partly spiritual, yet he is a single entity. One aim or result of the Christian world view is the recognition of, and the consistent unification of, the physical and spiritual aspects of the human being. In the diagram, the human personality occupies a position on

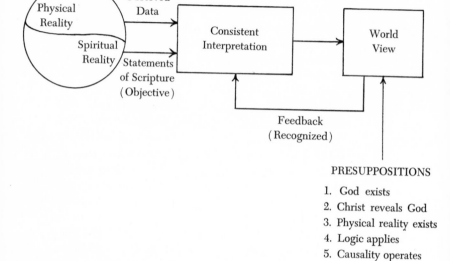

FIGURE 2. A Rationally Consistent Christian World View

the boundary line between physical and spiritual reality, and partakes of experiences originating in both spheres. Some of these remarks will be amplified later; all of them reflect ineffable truths that connect into the infinite and mysterious supernatural personality of God.

The diagram as shown in Figure 2 fails to illustrate explicitly a salient feature of any truly Christian view, namely, that it is a way of life and only within that context is it a mere way of thinking. This results from the revealed datum that the Christian means of knowing is existential: it is something one must become personally involved in. Christianity is not an academic intellectual exercise. It is a point of view that gives meaning to every area of one's life, and that meaning relates one vitally to the eternal purposes of the sovereign God. His spiritual sovereignty implies that our spiritual fulfillment as creature-humans is attained through our personal acquiescence and involvement in His purposes, through submission to God. Failure of much of organized Christianity to submit (individually or collectively) to God's revealed will, despite its lip service, has resulted in its evident failure to demonstrate an adequate or satisfying meaning for modern life.

The comprehensive Christian view illustrated in the diagram implicitly provides a full way of life for the whole man; potential is there for both intellectual and moral consistency. We humans, who hope and need to find purpose and meaning in life through our world views, comprise a complex of intellectual, emotional, and moral psycho-physiological drives. Our quest for purpose in existence involves us in a personal inquiry that transcends (but does not deny) mere descriptions of the physical and temporal. We may not rest until we glimpse the spiritual and eternal context. The Christian view, in providing needed meaning, takes proper account of the fact that we belong to both physics and spirit.

IV: *The Whole Man*

One proposition of this book is that Biblical Christianity can be made rationally consistent. We have defined all the basic terms in that statement in previous chapters. Of course, other world views also may be made rationally consistent. However, another proposition set forth here is that rational consistency alone is not a sufficient condition for adequacy of a world view. The needs of the human personality ought also to be satisfied by one's philosophy of life.

These personality needs are complex, and even their physically observable aspects are imperfectly understood by the relatively young science of psychology. How the Christian world view interacts with all the facets of personality is a vast and specialized topic and far beyond our scope here. But, because of the just-mentioned criterion for adequacy of a world view, it is necessary to correlate briefly here some Christian and psychological concepts.

A. NEEDS OF HUMAN NATURE

1. *Some Psychological Data and Their Interpretation*

(a) Human Nature

The English psychotherapist, Professor J. G. McKenzie, has described basic human nature as he and other psychol-

79

ogists have observed it in clinical practice.[1] Human nature
comprises a group of personality needs: the biological needs
— self-preservation, reproduction; the social needs — for
affection, for status; the personality needs — "to realize the
personality as a harmonious whole both in its inner and
outer relations"; the need for "Moral and Rational Unity"
— for purpose and meaning in life.

Following this, McKenzie then summarizes:[2]

> . . . original human nature . . . begins with certain specific
> needs in the interests of which we acquire behaviour ten-
> dencies by which we satisfy these needs. [These needs are
> interdependent, and find their meaning in the organism and
> personality which they subserve] . . . In virtue of man's
> capacity to perceive relations,[3] he can [by his will] subordi-
> nate both the needs and the behaviour-tendencies to his own
> selfish pleasures or ends. Immediately there is set up either
> a conflict which may result in neurosis, or a condition in
> which the possibility of realizing a personality at all is under-
> mined.
>
> Man's needs are not exhausted in a catalogue of biological
> impulses or ends. He is a self with an individuality of his
> own. *The very nature of that self is to realize his personality
> as a whole* (Italics ours).[4]

Many psychiatrists have written of the unity of the mind.
Ernest R. White, in a quite readable and excellent book
for the layman,[5] states:

> The mind is one, and all the names given to its various
> functions are not representatives of different things, they are

[1] Or, more precisely, as he and other psychologists have interpreted
their observations.

[2] *Nervous Disorders and Religion* (1947), abbreviated *NDR* hereafter, Chapter 1.

[3] This is close to the definition of "soul" given by some Bible scholars
— McKenzie defines the "soul" to be the "self," the organizing principle
of personality.

[4] *NDR*, pp. 60-61.

[5] E. R. White, *Christian Life and the Unconscious* (1959), p. 24.

different aspects of the same thing. . . Man is not a body, or a mind, or a spirit; he is a whole person, a fusion of all his parts.

The conscious and unconscious aspects of mind are in continuous interaction. This fact renders psychoanalysis and psychotherapy both possible and helpful.

These statements are interpretations placed upon data observed by these and other psychologists in the course of clinical and scientific investigations.[6] These statements are reasonable interpretations of such data, for they "make sense," correlate data, and establish principles by which to find meaning in other psychological experience.

(b) Personality Integration

As working hypotheses in our present discussion, we shall accept these concepts. Human nature includes the need for moral and rational integration of personality, the need for purposes and meaning in life, and the need for a sense of security and harmony in one's total environment.[7] The fact that we can be conscious of our own divisions, of the flesh warring against the spirit within us, is a proof of the basic character of these needs in human personality. Only such a drive for unity could make us aware of such divisions.

By "integration" we mean the process or result of harmonizing these drives and behavior tendencies. For harmony there must be consistency and there must be guiding principles by

[6] See, for a larger bibliography, the series of articles by Vernon Grounds in 1962-3 *His* magazine.

[7] In the developing science of psychology, the need for meaning in life as a requisite for personality integration — indeed the concept of personality integration — is a controversial subject. The view given here is held by many besides those quoted or referenced, and is related to what is sometimes called the "existential psychology" school. See, for example, Werner Wolff, *Values and Personality* (1950). See also Royce, *op. cit.*, an experimental psychologist who recognizes an inherent human need for values. See also Orville S. Walters, "Metaphysics, Religion and Psychotherapy," *Journal of the Christian Medical Society*, Winter 1959, p. 6.

which these needs and tendencies can be fitted together without mutual contradiction.

Among the aspects of personality involved in the processes of integration are the will and the conscience. The will is the ability of the self to choose goals consciously, to direct the personality toward them, and to inhibit the self from purely impulsive action or from actions inconsistent with conscience.

The conscience is the organ of the need for moral integration. It is the dynamic tendency of the self to coordinate and control behavior according to consciously or unconsciously accepted ethical, religious, and cultural standards. It reminds us of moral contradictions in our lives, of inconsistency between the accepted standard and our actual behavior. It is an unreliable censor, and may produce inordinately intense negative feelings. Some personality disorders arise from overactive prohibitive conscience, and some from repression of conscience.

Conscience itself is not a socially created entity, but is an inherent part of human personality. However, conscience does operate with social and cultural data. The ancient story of the Spartan boy shows this. According to Spartan morality it was not wrong to steal, but it was wrong to show weakness. The boy stole a fox. When caught, he quietly let himself be gnawed by the stolen fox under his cloak rather than cry out and show weakness. His cultural mores determined the particular acts which were acceptable, his conscience acted to regulate his behavior, and his will kept him from crying out, an act which would have been inconsistent with personality needs for moral integration and social status. Conscience thus does not itself determine what is right or wrong, but rather it reminds our wills of what the cultural context defines as morality.

The incident illustrates the psychological fact that humans are moral beings. We have moral as well as rational aspects. (We are not yet dealing overtly with the spiritual characteristics of man.) Consciously, we are a complex of emotion, will, and intellect; unconsciously we are a complex of interrelations between these personality facets and the set of needs that comprise human nature. Thus, we need ethical standards related to meaning in life. Without them our personalities automatically are in conflict, whether we are aware of it or not.

> The lack of a philosophy of life is always a sign of immaturity, for no man can be said to be well adjusted to life unless he has come to terms with . . . 'The Riddle of Life.'[8]

Jung[9] states that a psychoneurosis is to be understood in terms of the suffering of a person who has not discovered the meaning of his life.

(c) Man's Need for Extrascientific Meaning

These statements, when translated from the psychiatrist's technical jargon in which they are couched, are equivalent to observations made by astute philosophers since the earliest days. The human need for purpose is basic to our nature and, paraphrasing Augustine, we are restless (i.e., in conflict) until we find rest in some meaning to life. In modern times theologian Paul Tillich[10] has decried the tendency of the scientific age to substitute means for ends, to reduce man's status from subject to object[11]; he cites as evidence the flood of "so-called existentialist art, literature and philosophy, expressions of emptiness, meaninglessness and life-anxiety . . . split consciousness, indifference and disintegration." Science has given us knowledge of nature and the means to use nature for our own ends. Many have fallen into the trap of thinking that science can or should supply the ends as well.

---

[8] NDR, p. 51.
[9] C. G. Jung, Modern Man in Search of a Soul.
[10] Paul Tillich's speech at M.I.T. Centennial, reported in Time, April 21, 1961, p. 57.
[11] An interesting discussion of this contemporary "dehumanizing" process is given by C. S. Lewis, in The Abolition of Man (1947).

When it fails to do so, such people decide there are no ends, only means — techniques, and more knowledge.

The earlier remarks on scientific method and its limitations expose this fallacy. Science *describes* nature, i.e., physical, observable reality. Inherently it does not and cannot supply absolute meaning to this reality. The observable fact of psychology is that we humans seek the meaning behind the physical reality we study by science. (This has been taken by some as a "proof" that such meaning exists. Actually, of course, we must all *assume* that *some* meaning exists. This philosophical assumption should be consistent with our scientific assumptions.) That we crave guiding principles, underlying purpose — meaning — by which to integrate personality both rationally and morally, together with the inability of science *per se* to supply that meaning, makes for the frustration felt widely in this characteristically neurotic age. It is the current expression of the human predicament.

The Christian world view we are describing in this book provides guiding principles that can structure both rational and moral integration of personality. As we have seen, intellectual consistency is possible because this view does not preclude acceptance and interpretation of any physically real or objective data.[12] The Christian should face all facts with complete intellectual honesty. No unconscious conflicts need arise within his mind because of repressed data. He is intellectually free, therefore, to develop personality, to satisfy his need for rational integration.

Unfortunately, not all Christians take advantage of their potential intellectual freedom; we commonly fail to let the truth set us free. The fact is that a personality cannot fully develop if data are being repressed. If, through faulty or

[12] See K. Horney, *The Neurotic Personality of Our Time* (1937), for a clear discussion of various factors involved in neurosis. Although she explicitly discusses neither meaning to life nor religion, and her view is that of a clinical psychoanalyst, her remarks are consistent with our point here. It is beyond our scope to treat such a technical topic.

narrow interpretation of scripture, a Christian person decides he cannot accept observed data of science, his data
repression can lead to conflict. Conversely, if through bias
or indifference, a scientist ignores his need for harmony with
whatever spiritual forces there are, he is repressing data.
The conflict engendered by failure or inability to resolve
contradictions between data, interpretations, our moral natures, and our world views, is real conflict even if it be unconscious. It can twist and warp a personality as surely as
more obviously harmful moral conflicts. Repression or dodg-
ing of data by the mind verges on immorality, in any case,
since it is a form of dishonesty.

The means by which the Christian world view structures
the moral integration of a personality will be discussed after
the need for moral unity is more sharply focussed.

2. *Blocks to Moral Integration*

(a) Guilt

Two types of guilt need to be distinguished here. There
is legal guilt, the fact that one has violated a law. This type
of guilt is as objective as the law is specific, and may be
associated with consequences if the law so provides. Justice
involves the determination of legal guilt or innocence before,
the law, and assignment of legal consequences or penalties.
Legal guilt depends only upon whether one has demonstrably
transgressed a specific article of law, and may be unrelated to
the person's own feelings about his action.

On the other hand, psychological guilt is the feeling one
has when his conscience condemns him; it is his own attitude
toward his real self. This type of guilt is a subjective thing,
a feeling, an attitude, rather than an objective matter of relationship to law. Yet psychological guilt is very real, and
makes its existence felt within the personality. When behavior is contrary to the dictates (law) of conscience, regardless of the rationality of those dictates, guilt feelings arise.

These guilt feelings may be unrelated to actual transgressions of any external law.

(b) The Christian Concept of Sin

The revealed data of the Christian view show us that God is a sovereign and loving Person, to whom we, His created children, owe full allegiance and love. He is worthy of worship. He is perfect in every respect in senses of this term we can barely comprehend. Our own limited and, as we shall see shortly, perverted senses of what God ought to be cannot help but fall short of the actual ultimate truth. A Christian has realized his inherent human inability to know God by his own reasoning powers, and he trusts (assumes) the accuracy of the revelation God has given us in Jesus Christ, recorded by inspiration in the Bible.

The fact of God's glorious perfection clarifies the Christian concept of sin. Sin is deviation from God's perfect will or, amounting to the same thing, it is rebellion against the rightful authority of God, either by willful action or neglectful failure to recognize His sovereignty. Christ taught that attitudes, being father to the actions, are the more important aspect of human sinfulness. "From within, out of the hearts of men, proceed evil thoughts. . . ." The state of a man who does not recognize God is a sinful state, characterized by self-will rather than acquiescence to God's will. This state of being determines attitudes and, to some extent, actions. The same act performed with recognition of God's presence or in willful ignorance of God's claims upon us, is holy and good in one case and sinful and rebellious in the other. "A proud look, and the plowing of the wicked, is sin" (Prov. 21:4).

Of course, the scriptures reveal some specific divine commands, the transgression of which is sin, and obedience to which is expected as the norm. Because these commands are specific, e.g., "Thou shalt not kill," sins of transgression of these commands are objective, and they lead to legal guilt before God. All other acts we perform are inherently morally neutral, and acquire a holy or sinful character through our attitude toward God as we perform them. From a purely human point of view, the moral quality of such acts cannot be assessed. Therefore we are not to judge others. However, it is written, "God sees not as man sees, for man looks upon external appearances, whereas God looks upon the heart." God knows our attitudes toward Himself, and He and only He is able righteously to judge our goodness or sinfulness. Because He perfectly understands our frame, and because He knows the motives underlying all our actions, His judgment not only is just, but it is objective. God's revealed blanket condemnation of the human race is that "all have sinned, and come short" of His glory, i.e., we have all individually rebelled against the authority of God and have acted in self-will. Because His judgment of us is objectively true, as a race we are individually legally guilty before a holy God. To the extent that a person recognizes his personal responsibility to his Creator, this legal guilt can also become psychological guilt.

(c) Sin as Egocentricity

In psychological terms sin is "egocentricity," a condition in which all impulses, all behavior is directed toward one's self. Motivation is self-aggrandizement, whether the resulting action is apparently holy and charitable or bestial and cruel.

> Egocentricity, which is *Sin* and not *a Sin* pollutes the whole activity of the individual to such a degree that it is the principle of that individual's personality . . . Every neurosis may be interpreted in terms of protecting the egocentric self, or of getting it something. . . .[13]

Egocentricity, in simple terms, is selfishness. This basic human tendency toward self-exaltation and self-assertiveness,

---

[13] J. G. McKenzie, *Psychology, Psychotherapy, and Evangelicalism* (1940), pp. 135ff. Abbreviated hereafter as *PPE*.

directed inward, is to be contrasted with the principle of love, which is object-centered, i.e., directed outward toward others.

God alone is absolutely object-centered, i.e., purely love, and purely unselfish. "Love seeketh not her own," and "God is love," the Bible tells us. "God gave Himself" for our reconciliation. No man meets this standard of love, for egocentricity tinges our deepest love, sentiments, and often contaminates our holiest acts. Here, from a psychological point of view, we see an ubiquitous attitude of self-will, a concept consistent with the Christian's revealed data regarding sin.[14]

(d) Guilt as a Sense of Need

Many psychologists hold that guilt is always destructive to personality. Certainly unresolved guilt feelings are disruptive, for the basically egocentric person must repress them. As long as it is no more than fear of punishment by an angry vindictive God, or by an outraged society, then this guilt is "an emotion experienced in the downward thrust of repression . . . generated by the infantile prohibitive conscience and not by the adult positive conscience."[15] Such guilt is damaging to the full development of personality because it distorts our consciousness of God. A person in the throes of fearful guilt, anxious concerning his real or fancied sins, tends to overemphasize the character of God as Judge, and to project upon Him the threatening of his own infantile conscience.

As we have seen, Christianity shows us that God is not only a holy, omnipotent, and righteous Judge, but also is a loving Heavenly Father who seeks fellowship with the God-conscious human race. Man's deviation from God's revealed norms for attitudes and behavior (that is, sin) severs that fellowship. A sense of consciousness of our sin is necessary

---

[14] See Mowrer, *The Crisis in Religion and Psychiatry* (1961), for the views of yet another psychologist on sinfulness.

[15] McKenzie, *PPE*, pp. 124ff.

for us in our approach to God. Without this realization of our personal need for forgiveness we are more likely to approach God, if at all, as the Pharisee rather than as the Publican. Christ's teaching is that forgiveness is possible, but only to those who recognize their need.[16] The love of God our Father has made this forgiveness available; Jesus Christ Himself has reconciled us to God. "The grace of God . . . brings salvation."

This sense of sin, requisite for our approach to God, is the type of guilt feeling that tends toward repentance and thus toward resolution of guilt and personality conflict. This sense of sin is to be contrasted with the selfish fear-of-punishment-centered guilt; it is not a projection of an infantile conscience, but it is a true and objective recognition of one's own inadequacy — of one's legal guilt as sinner before the bar of God's justice. It is remorse that one has till now ignored and spurned God's proffered love. One sees God as loving Father as well as holy Judge. Since "perfect love casts out fear," the real basis for the sense of sin, the "godly sorrow which leads to repentance," is the realization that our sin is rebellion against that loving God. If this fact is brought home to us by gaining some new insights into the character of God, then we suffer shame at having violated and refused God's love toward us. This is the true repentance leading the sinner to seek forgiveness and reconciliation with God.

The more disruptive type of psychological guilt may, of course, precede the truer, positive, sense of sin. Often it leads to emotional upheavals in "conversion," which for normal people settle into more solid foundations for Christian personality, but which may also lead to further instabilities in others. The latter cases must be regarded as aberrant by the consistent Christian, and are readily explained as such. If one's conviction of sin is based on disruptive psychological guilt feelings, based on pure (egocen-

[16] Luke 5:31-32: They that are whole need not a physician, but those who recognize that they are sick.

tric) fear for self, then it may be that no true repentance or sorrow for sin ever takes place. Such a one may raise his hand at a tent meeting, or "hit the sawdust trail," but it is unlikely that he will have a true conversion. The true basis for fellowship with God is missing; he lacks the repentance and *sorrow for sin because of what sin is,* a rebuff of God's love and an affront to God's righteous law. The name of Christ has been dishonored by many who never have actually taken that name as their own, except in the course of an emotional upheaval. Not having turned away from their sin toward God, that is, never having repented due to never having had a truly Christian sense of sin, these people were not truly converted. They hear the word, spring up, but the first hot sun withers them because they didn't have roots any deeper than their own emotions.

Fortunately, an emotional upheaval can also lead to the true sense of sin and repentance. A person may have begun with fearful guilt, or with an infantile conscience, but may then come to realize the inadequacy of his own feelings of guilt to bring him to God. Then he may find that although his own feelings, as well as anything else he himself may bring, are inadequate *per se,* yet the reconciling work of Christ and the magnetic love of God draw him to true sorrow for sin, and to a personal acceptance of Jesus Christ as the means of forgiveness. A tendency toward some personality instability is not automatically nor instantaneously removed, but the foundation is laid for a more mature person.[17] As one grows in grace and knowledge of Christ, that is, as one becomes more deeply personally involved in a consistent Christian world view, he finds real peace and joy in believing. He finds his various personality needs being met, gains potential to become a full mature person — a whole man.

This is the normal Christian pattern: from natural man,

17 That foundation is Christ Himself (I Cor. 3:11).

enslaved to self-willed sin, and full of repressions of one's own guilt before God; through repentance and pardon to resolution and recognized forgiveness, and on to full development of an integrated personality that is free to serve God. The human personality, in the Christian view, was created by God with the capability of experiencing remorse for sin, the psychological guilt that leads the sinner to seek God. The disruptive type of guilt feelings would seem to be a perversion of this divinely intended use of psychological guilt.

B. RESOLUTION OF GUILT

1. *Psychological Conditions*

We have seen how guilt arising in the personality from conflict between one's willful actions and one's conscience can disrupt personality integration. A person who is aware of spiritual requirements, e.g., who recognizes God's sovereignty, but whose egocentricity puts him in conflict with those requirements, is also a candidate for neurosis if he represses the spiritually real data impinging on him. However, if such a one faces up to his sin, seeing it as God sees it — as rebellion — and in true repentance seeks God's forgiveness, then it is revealed to us that a new relationship with God can be established.

> Let the wicked forsake his way and the unrighteous man his thoughts: and let him return unto the Lord, and He will have mercy upon him; and to our God for He will abundantly pardon (Isa. 55:7).

According to Professor McKenzie,[18]

> To understand forgiveness from the psychological point of view it is necessary, not only to realize the effect of sin upon *our* spiritual relations, but also its effects upon those whom we sinned against.
>
> . . . Forgiveness is the restoration of the spiritual relationship; the status of the sinner is re-created [to that status en-

18 *PPE*, pp. 140ff.

joyed before the sin, and as though the relationship had never been broken by his sin].

Two fundamental conditions must be fulfilled before forgiveness is really and truly experienced. One applies to the sinner, the other to the person wronged, in this case God. On the human side, as we have already seen, there must be repentance. This is a spiritual condition in which thought, emotion, and will are all involved. On the cognitive side there is the knowledge of what was done, of responsibility for what was done . . . Then the emotion of shame, humiliation and remorse arising out of [this intellectual recognition of sin]. Finally the conational [willful] turning from sin, from egocentricity to objectcentricity. All this is involved in repentance. . . [The whole personality is fully and deeply involved in it].

[The other condition] must be fulfilled by the forgiver. *He must feel the sin as though it were his own* (Italics McKenzie's). These are the psychological conditions of forgiveness — repentance of the sinner, and the vicarious suffering of the person wronged. We have analyzed no case of human forgiveness which has not fulfilled these two conditions. . . .

Repentance is the turning to God in response to a realization of His love and to the sense of remorse at our previous rejection of that love. It is a widely misunderstood term, possibly because the norms of society, by which our consciences set standards, are sufficiently subverted and degraded from the will of God for mankind, that most "decent" people reject the notion that *they themselves* are sinners.

However, it is revealed that we are all objectively guilty to some degree, and if at all, then we must feel, consciously or unconsciously, the tension which arises from the sense of guilt.

Most people seem to be able to repress this sense of guilt. Most of us do not feel ourselves to be very bad people, at least no worse than anybody else. According to the psychological principles we have been discussing, repression of guilt is a step toward neurosis. Within a society where everybody is doing it, however, where sanity is statistical, a slight case of guilt-repression passes unnoticed. Coupled with other, especially bizarre, personality disorders, it might lead one to visit an analyst. But most of us get along with our problems, and live them down.[19] Only occasionally do we pause to wonder if we are missing something in life.

For some of us, the sense of guilt before God leads us to respond to the love of God whereby we receive forgiveness and resolve the guilt. Such a person has the potential to achieve a balanced personality, although he may find himself out of step in a neurotic society. Even a person who is not a great sinner in the world's view, when he understands the holiness and love of God, and sees his objective guilt and need for forgiveness, and his rejection of God's love, will see himself as "the chief of sinners." Thus he is in a position to repent, that is, to turn to God and seek His righteousness first. This is the first condition for forgiveness.

2. *Christian Data — The Good News*

The Christian gospel shows how the second condition for experienced forgiveness is met. The wronged One feels that sin against Him as His own, because of who Jesus Christ is and what He did. If Jesus Christ were not God Incarnate — God's own spiritual nature embodied in a human form to reveal Himself to us — then He could not feel our weaknesses and sins as He must for true forgiveness. If Jesus Christ the LORD had not "Himself bore our sins in His body on the tree, that we might die to sin and live to righteousness," we could never be forgiven.[20] If there is any point that is clearly revealed, it is that "Christ died for our sins, according to the scriptures."[21] There may be room for different theories of

---

[19] Sometimes by "living it up!"
[20] I Peter 2:24.
[21] I Corinthians 15:3.

mechanism of the atonement, but the Christian data refer repeatedly to the *fact* of the atonement. Christ is the "Lamb of God which takes away the sin of the world." Only thus could he really "know our frame, that we are dust." Hebrews 2:14-18, Phillips version[22] puts it:

> Since then 'the children' have a common physical nature as human beings, He also became a human being, so that by going through death as a man He might destroy him who had the power of death, that is the devil; and might also set free those who lived their whole lives a prey to the fear of death. It is plain that for this purpose He did not become an angel; He became a *man,* in actual fact a descendant of Abraham. It was imperative that He should be made like His brothers in nature, if He were to become a High Priest both compassionate and faithful in the things of God, and at the same time able to make atonement for the sins of the people. For by virtue of His own suffering under temptation He is able to help those who are exposed to temptation.

The means of true forgiveness are at hand. Both psychological conditions are realized for a person who meets the first one by true repentance. By faith we come to God, cast our recognized unrepressed guilt upon His mercy, and receive His forgiveness gratefully. Such saving faith is compounded of will and decision, of intellectual consistency, and of emotional elements as well.

McKenzie concludes:[23]

> There is an implicit belief in an object [the person of Christ], there is the outgoing trust in the object; and there is the inner confidence generated by the object . . . We believe that the subjective authority which the content of our faith exercises over us will be found in the capacity of the object to resolve our conflicts or to satisfy the need for moral and rational unity and the prospective, spiritual aim of personality.

---

[22] *Letters to Young Churches* (1957). This passage in Hebrews 2 is especially well expressed to clarify the point being made here.
[23] *PPE,* p. 198.

C. PURPOSE AND MEANING IN LIFE FOR THE WHOLE MAN

1. *Overcoming Egocentricity*

We have discussed rational and moral integration of a personality as though they were separate matters. They are distinct but, owing to the unitary nature of personality, these two aspects also are interdependent. In the Christian view, as illustrated in Figure 2, the human personality exists along the boundary line, and contains elements from both physics and spirit. The intellect is primarily involved in the processes of rational integration. These processes consist in interpreting observable physical data together with any other data one has into a harmonious structure of thought in such a way that data need not be ignored. The "other data" include, for the Christian, statements of the Bible, perhaps along with less objective experiences. In order for the intellect to interpret data, a rationally consistent world view must be assumed and used as the interpretive framework. Christianity contains such a view.

The will is largely involved in the processes of moral integration, whereby the personality acquires the ability, the desire, to act in accordance with the dictates of conscience. The conscience of a Christian is influenced as to its contents and sensitized in its reactions by the knowledge of God through Christ. However, the will decides by use of the intelligence, and acts through the emotional drives of a person. Further, intellectual honesty depends on the moral honesty of the will to preclude suppression of valid data. In these and even subtler ways the various organs of personality interact in the course of rational and moral integration.

But how is one to acquire an ability, a desire, to act in accordance with his conscience? Such an attitude can develop only if egocentricity, which in the Christian view is sin, ceases to be the dominant feature in one's personality. In other words, the moral integration of the personality can happen only if the person is changed from being egocentric. Christianity provides the means by which this can occur. Briefly stated, *one's turning to God and loving Him bring spiritual forces into action in one's personality which dominate the selfish principle.*[24] Purpose and meaning in life, foundational in the integration of personality, are found in love for God. This is why we have already emphasized that true Christianity, being more than merely a way of thinking, is a full way of life. In particular it is a way of life characterized by a relationship with God, a relationship of active love, whereby God Himself rules and overrules in our lives.

Professor McKenzie comments:

> . . . [The] self I believe to be a spiritual entity, and its drive for rational and moral unity is the source of the drive for meaning to life, and I should add, cannot stop short of entering into relations with whatever spiritual forces there are in the world.[25]

When a finite human personality comes into the vital relationship with the infinite spiritual person of God, that human soul is no longer left to drift whimsically among crosscurrents of its own egocentricity. Love for the Heavenly Father becomes a driving force and purpose. God Himself, according to Jesus' promise, begins to live in the human personality, regenerating it, and renewing the mind. Not only ethical standards are thus provided, but also the desire to meet the standards rather than to rebel against them in self-will. The ego is still present, but egocentricity, that is sin, is no longer the dominant trait of a person related to God.

2. *Knowing God Personally*

Let us examine the Christian's purpose in life, as he learns it from the revealed data. It is around this purpose and meaning of life that the organizing of personality elements ought to proceed for the Christian who accepts the three

[24] Romans 6:14, Philippians 2:13, Galatians 5:16-17.
[25] *NDR,* p. 122.

axioms of science and the two by which he may know God through Christ. Having realized his natural condition — estranged from God by his own willfulness — he has cast himself utterly upon God's mercy, and received the forgiveness made possible by Jesus Christ. Thus reconciled, he is no longer required, in the interests of his egocentric nature, to repress guilt feelings for his sin. He has faced this issue, and can begin to develop his personality as a whole. What then is the meaning of life to such a person? What are his purposes?

Paul summarized the answer to these questions in his declaration, "To me to live is Christ." He counted all things as refuse compared with the knowledge of Christ, giving up all "that I may win Christ, and be found in Him . . . [having] the righteousness of God. . . ." Similar, sometimes less succinct, statements of life's meaning and purpose were made or implied by others among the apostles and pre-Christian prophets. Jesus Christ Himself said that knowledge of the only true God constitutes life eternal. This is the personal knowledge that transcends mere acquaintance with historical facts, and involves us through all the personality, in the way we interact dynamically in knowing any person well. In this case the person we are getting to know is the infinite and holy, loving God and Father.

For a person who has seen himself a hopeless and shameful guilty rebel in the sight of God, the realization and personalization of God's mercy should evoke just such a reaction as that of Paul. To know Christ is to find meaning in life, for to know Him is to love Him, and to understand what love really is. The attitude of one who has begun to know Christ can never be wholly egocentric again. As we grow in knowing Him, as we get better acquainted personally, we become more object-centered, more loving, more like Him. This growth results from God's own further revealing of Himself, for the more important part of this personal interaction between us and God is God's part. Not only immortal-

ity is had in such knowledge, but full personality development — abundant life here and now — lies in this direction
as well.

3. *Love for God as the Purpose of Life*

These statements must sound downright unexciting to one
who has never experienced the sense of sin, the forgiveness
of God, nor come into the "light of God, shining in the face
of Jesus Christ." Similarly, statements regarding the joys and
bliss of a love-marriage[26] and family-raising fall on unrespon-
sive deaf ears of a bachelor or selfish (unlovingly) married
person. The illustration of a married couple is a good one,
used parabolically by both Christ and Paul, as well as by
Solomon, as an example of how love of God reorganizes our
lives. A young man or woman in love can tell how his or
her life was changed by knowing the object of love. A
loving married couple consists of two partners, trying to
please each other, each giving himself to the other more and
more, their love thereby deepening and maturing. Love here
is seen as a giving of one's *self*, a conscious suppression (not
repression) of selfishness and egocentric impulses to the
other. It is a baring of one's innermost self, with defense
mechanisms down, exposing tenderest thoughts and feelings
to the possibility of trampling by the other. Love grows as
we learn to know the other person so as not to trample on
these exposed nerve endings, nor to take offense when ours
are touched. Thus love learns new things, delights in the
person of the beloved, holds back nothing, is tenderly careful
of the beloved's feelings. This is an ideal, but practical, concept of love. Such love between people gives meaning to
their lives: they want to know and to love each other more
fully. Life is meant to give oneself this way, i.e., to love.
Such a love, in a fuller, more perfect sense even than here

---

[26] Assuming genuine other-person-centered love, which transcends
the purely physical aspects of love as personal knowledge transcends
factual data.

described, is the privilege of everyone who knows Christ
and responds to His love.

The illustration is imperfect, but the reconciled sinner loves
Jesus Christ as a wife does her husband. Christ has given
Himself fully, He emptied Himself, and our love for Him
now gives us meaning and purpose, redirecting our otherwise vain egos. We want to know Him better, and He wants
us to know ourselves better, too, so we can love, i.e., give
ourselves, more fully day by day. Thus do we finite humans
grow in the love relationship with the holy, infinite God,
whose very nature is Love. Humans were created to interact and respond lovingly to God's love. Until they do, they
long after the relationship, often substituting self-devised
cheap imitations for the real thing.[27] When we interact and
respond to God's love, our human natures begin to be trans-
formed, and to become capable of responding even more.
The human personality, a finite-dimensional projection of the
infinite person of God, is able to realize itself only as it finds
meaning in loving God. Only as we respond to God in "faith
that operates on the principle of love," can God consistently
energize our lives with His own life, and fulfill in us the desire and ability to live as we should, victorious over our
natural egocentricity.

4. *Personal Involvement*

(a) Willingness to Know Truth

The world view we propose is a way of life, and a way
of life must be lived. Christianity in this view is "abundant"
living, a life fully lived, a faith honestly issuing in consistent
actions, ultimately interacting with every facet of personality,
providing meaning and purpose within the total data-context.
Our intellects, our emotions, and our wills are active in their

[27] See Jeremiah 2:13, for an indictment; also Romans 1:25. The Old
Testament history of Israel is replete with examples of this kind of
spiritual prostitution.

respective fashions in living the life, in walking in the way of life.

Honest appraisal of the total data-context, the full sphere of reality, leads to honest personal application of the truths found therein. Science, as we have seen, is amoral, i.e., neutral on the ethical quality of personal actions. Sociology or psychology may some day be able to predict or describe cultural and personal interactions which lead to violence or war, but the moral tone of suffering, pain, and death needs to be interjected by defining these things as "evil." This is the way of science and metascience. Thus the truths that apply to our personal action ultimately spring from the specifically Christian revelation of God to us. Our willingness to re-evaluate our existing interpretations, to recognize our limitations, to be convinced, to act on implications of the truths we discover — in short, our honesty in approaching truths — is the key to knowledge of those truths.

Willingness to follow truth through to personal involvement is the foundation of Christian epistemology. Jesus Christ Himself enunciated this principle: "If any man is willing to do God's will, he shall know about the teaching, whether it is from God . . ." (John 7:17). This statement was made, in the course of a long discussion, to openly antagonistic and closed-minded Pharisees, as well as to others who were interested but uncommitted. The principle should not surprise us too much; even at a human level, to understand any point of view, one must get into a frame of mind where he is willing to be convinced. Conviction presages action. Christ tells us that we cannot understand the God He reveals to us unless we are willing to be convinced into appropriate action. Without this willingness, the revelation becomes incomprehensible, because involvement of only the intellectual aspect of personality is incomplete involvement. Christianity makes little sense to one who is not fully involved personally. Our willingness, the possibility of becoming committed to the point of performance, is the key by which God opens our minds further, and floods us with knowledge of Himself.

(b) Dynamically Interacting Faith

Christian faith is a positive concept.[28] Faith is trust in a person, acceptance of data objectively revealed by and through that person, leading to such a personal relationship between the believer and God that the believer comes to "know" God. He "hath given us an understanding that we might know Him that is true."

Packer says:[29]

> Having disclosed Himself objectively in history, in His incarnate son, and in His written scriptural word, God now enlightens men subjectively in experience so that they apprehend his self-disclosure for what it is. Thus He causes them to know Him, and His end in revelation is achieved.

Our faith begins in acknowledging God's trustworthiness and in recognizing Jesus Christ as His means of revealing Himself. Faith continues in willful action, whereby we submit to God's recognized authority, through which further light and knowledge are given. Note that the Christian's faith is strengthened by the personal interactions between himself and God. A new class of data — spiritual and subjective as contrasted with the spiritual and objective statements of scripture — is provided to the believer. These new data, these experiences of knowing God's working in one's life, are common to consistent practicing Christians. They, too, are to be fitted rationally into the comprehensive world view, along with objective physical data, and they tend to form for the Christian incontrovertible evidence of the truth, an effective "shield of faith."

Christian belief is thus a rational, positive, and personal acceptance of the authoritative Christ. Anything less than this

---

[28] Recommended reading: J. G. Machen, *What is Faith?* (1946); also J. I. Packer, *op. cit.*, Chapter V.

[29] J. I. Packer, *op. cit.*, p. 118.

is at best inconsistent Christianity. Irrational faith under-
estimates and misunderstands the nature of God and His
revelation. Negative faith, a denunciation of the false, is
sterile, a dead or moribund mockery of the "abundant life"
proclaimed by Christ. Impersonal faith is a contradiction in
terms, for we find meaning in life and in the universe around
us only in proportion to our involvement at all levels and
facets of personality.[30] True Christian faith is a personal
commitment, a giving of oneself, as wholly as one is able at
whatever one's state of personality development, to the ac-
knowledged truths of God.

These three elements of faith are likewise necessary to
consistent Christianity. Remove any one of them, rationality,
positive approach, or personal acceptance, and we not only
deny scriptural teaching, but we find that chinks appear in
the logical consistency of the whole Christian world view.
For example, remove the element of personal commitment
from the definition of faith. Christianity is then reduced to a
mere intellectual exercise. The psychology of the atonement,
by which we can understand something of how God justly
forgives us, loses its impact. Unless we are truly repentant
in a committed personal faith, God's justice and mercy do not
meet, His righteousness and truth do not kiss; we are not
reconcilable. We remain in the morass of our own making,
our waywardness; we are left to dig our own dry wells in the
attempt to satiate our spiritual thirst. The waters which would
flow (as Jesus promised) from our innermost being are
stopped unless we involve that innermost being in the knowledge of the love of God by means of fully personal faith.

These things are understood with difficulty by the person
who knows only that he has a need for something but knows
not what it is he needs. It is a leap of faith to abandon oneself to Christ, but having done this, one finds what he has
been seeking all along. Meaning to life is here, in knowing

[30] This statement is true of any rational point of view, no matter
what its articles of faith, e.g., even scientism or humanism.

Christ. Submission to the authority of God, and the implications of the Lordship of Christ to the individual personality, may seem, for one yet uncommitted, too high a price to pay, especially since most of the world presents a cacophony of dissenting opinion. However, in the Christian view our personal submission to the rightful Lordship of Christ is, paradoxically, the key to personal freedom. Otherwise we are slaves to self, bound to sin, and intrinsically incapable of pleasing God. The freedom of the loving heart can be realized only by abandoning oneself completely to the God of love.

5. *Conclusion*

Christ's summary commandment is "love the Lord your God with all your heart, all your soul, all your strength, and all your mind." This command indicates the means of satisfying the basic needs of our personalities. These basic human needs for integration of personality involve our minds, our wills, and our emotions. With our intellects we organize our perceptions into consistent patterns — the scientific method is a means to this end. Integration requires a world view that supplies some meaning to the consistent, but philosophically neutral, descriptions of the physical reality in which we are immersed. Personality integration also proceeds in our moral lives, where our wills organize our personal motives into consistent patterns. The same world view structures both intellectual and moral aspects of the unified personality, and this imposes the double criteria for world view adequacy. Not only must we allow for rational consistency, but also provide the means of moral consistency. Not only must our view accommodate all observable data and deny none, but also it must provide suitable meaning to our human existence. It must provide meaning and purpose that not only allows, but also enables us to act consistently within assumed philosophical or religious views, that is, within our understanding of the extrascientific or teleological realities in which we are also immersed.

Because of human egocentricity, or selfishness, we tend to be in unconscious conflict. Acting selfishly is inconsistent with the world view ethic; repression of the inconsistency, or failing to face up to our egocentricity, leads to guilt, and guilt narrows the personality, disabling it even more to act consistently.

The Christian views God as the sovereign Ruler, the all wise and eternal self-existent Creator, the holy and just Judge, and the loving Heavenly Father who has revealed Himself. Human egocentricity is an affront to God, since it asserts the creature's independence from the Creator and rejects the highest good that God lovingly proffers. The Christian recognizes this fact, and in accepting the free gift of God's love — forgiveness — receives the enabling power of God to live a life that can please God. The basis for forgiveness is the atonement of Christ. The personal recognition and response to God's love turns the human personality around from egocentricity, freeing the human spirit from slavery to selfishness.

Thus we see how moral integration of the personality is made possible in the Christian world view, by a conscious departure from the egocentric. Love, wholly object-centered and specifically *love of God,* whose children we are, *is the means* and, since our view is dynamically developing, it *is also the end.* This purpose in life for the Christian is thus one which can and must structure unification of personality. Satisfaction of the other human nature needs fits into place around rational and moral integration. *Human personality* as conceived by the psychologist and, more important, as revealed by God to us as being His will for us, *is achievable within the consistent Christian world view.* The possibility exists for us who believe, and only for us who believe, of becoming whole men.

V: *Specific Scientific Problems of the Christian World View*

Space forbids us to attempt a thorough study in this section of how data may be interpreted in the Christian view. We believe that fully consistent interpretations are possible, although perhaps unknown, for all physically observed and divinely revealed data. We shall indicate a few classical problem areas and suggest possible means of reinterpreting some data in a consistent way. We are here making no final pronouncements or dogmatic assertions on the few subjects treated. It is hoped that these indicated solutions will stimulate thought and lead the way for the reader to interpret the basic data involved in other problems he may encounter. These other problems are, as the physics textbooks say, left as "exercises for the student."[1]

---

[1] One such interesting question is the following: What if life is made in a test tube some day? Another: What if sentient, or even religious, beings are found on other planets some day? Aside from the speculative and academic character of these problems, they would serve as good practice for a Christian student in applying his world view. Suffice it to say that these events would be explainable within the Christian framework given here.

A. Biblical Interpretation

1. *The Bible as History*

(a) The Historical Problem

On its face, the Bible is an historical document, and some of the problems in its interpretation stem from this fact. In determining what has happened in the past, we are always at the mercy of some person's (or persons') ability to observe and/or record his (their) observations. Added to this problem of historical inquiry may be the problems of interpreting these reports from within long-gone cultural contexts and dead languages. Further, events are always interrelated, and human observers are always limited in what they can see and record — limited by space and time if not mentally or otherwise. Thus, even if we have an accurate record of some events, it is necessarily incomplete, for many perhaps crucially related events may not be recorded.

From this we see that historical data are always *selected* from among the historical facts or actual happenings, sometimes by the early reporters, sometimes by the vagaries of climate and war. It is one of the features of historical data as distinguished from "scientific" data. We must be careful to apply this principle in our brief study of the Bible as history, as we use the available data to piece together the most accurate picture we can of what actually happened in the past. We shall here restrict the discussion to a few of those events which are intimately related to Biblical history. The data available include: the Bible itself; many historical documents of contemporary societies, which have come to us through archaeological research; and other artifacts. These varied sources of historical information all contain selected data. What is found in these records might be an accurate report as far as it goes, or it might not. An artifact is only a tiny peephole into the culture which produced it. The writer of any historical document has had some criteria to guide his selection of data for that document. He has some purpose in writing, which may or may not allow elastic handling of the truth as he knows it.

An example of the influence of the historians' purposes is seen in the comparison between the Assyrian record of Sennacherib's invasion of Palestine (circa 700 B.C.) and the Biblical record (II Kings 18:13-19:37). The Bible says that Sennacherib took many cities, but that some catastrophe overtook him during his siege of Jerusalem. The Assyrian chronicler plays up the conquest of Lachish and other walled cities, exults in the captives, and praises Sennacherib and the Assyrian gods. He mentions the siege of Jerusalem, but says nothing of its capture, nor of the calamity. Herodotus mentions mice in his recounting of this incident, and an outbreak of plague among the Assyrian troops is thought to have been the catastrophe. The purpose of the Assyrian was to tell the world what a great warrior Sennacherib was. The purpose of the Jewish chronicler who recorded these events was to show how God answered the prayer of the chastened King Hezekiah. In this case the two records can be correlated — the Assyrian's silence is significant, and an additional data source (Herodotus) is available. In other cases, present evidence from extra-Biblical sources is too meager to make a good correlation. In a very few cases there is outright conflict between sources, but it is significant that new achaeological discovery has always tended to confirm the accuracy of the Bible.[2]

The purpose of the historian must, therefore, intrude itself into the history he records for us. His intentions, no matter how honorable, must influence his choice of what facts to order and array from among the vast confusion of data that characterizes contemporary events. The later historian, who has an advantage of some historical perspective, but who by

[2] W. F. Albright, *Archaeology of Palestine* (1954); see also G. E. Wright and D. N. Freedman, eds., *Biblical Archaeology Reader* (1961), hereafter referred to as *BAR*; and G. Barton, *Biblical Archaeology* (1936).

being removed from the actual events has only partial data to guide him, must also let his reasons for writing influence his choice of material. Hence, all historical data are "processed" data, that is, they have received some interpretation in the very recording.

These principles are applicable to the study of Biblical history as well as of secular history. The men who penned the Old and New Testaments wrote with a purpose; they selected from among the facts they witnessed, or from among earlier historical accounts, and wrote. The result is no less than history; the Bible is an accurate and unique historical record, dealing with peoples of whom we would otherwise know essentially nothing. What has been written in the Bible concerning these ancient times and peoples has, in instances where corroboration is possible, generally harmonized with other (secular) historical records. There is no scientific reason to dispute the factual accuracy of the Biblical history, especially in view of the principles we have cited here that govern all historical data.

(b) The Purpose of Biblical History

To understand the Bible as history, we must seek the Bible's own statements regarding its composition, and specifically concerning the purposes for which it was written. Such a study illustrates the Christian assumption that God reveals Himself through Jesus Christ, which implies that the historical data given throughout all the Bible subserve that personal revelation. Since it is God who is showing us something of Himself, Bible history has a special objectivity. That is, these historical data are divinely selected and interpreted to form an integral part of God's purposeful revelation. This statement follows logically from the Christian assumptions and from the character of historical data. In the sense that Biblical statements are a part of God's revelation to us, they are "raw data" to be fitted into some such rational world view scheme as we have discussed. In the sense that some of these statements, as history, are also based on actual historical events, they are "processed data," and this fact also needs to be considered in our rationalization.

Accuracy in the historical data of the Bible is a consequence of the consistency of God who reveals Himself. It is important that Abraham, Isaac, Jacob, Joseph and others actually lived and were not merely characters in an historical novel. It is important because Christ Himself considered them real historical people. It is important because a God of truth cannot consistently reveal Himself in deception. It is important because God's dealings with us real people of later times are exemplified and patterned after His dealings with the real flesh and blood people of Biblical history, whose weaknesses and strengths, sins and repentances are like ours. The recorded dealings of God with these men and women are a part of God's revelation to us, for they look ahead to, i.e., prophesy of, Christ (I Cor. 10:1-12).

Jesus Christ is not merely one of the *dramatis personae* of a morality play. He spoke of others as though they too were real. We may not conclude from His silence that still others were purely parabolic, illustrative, or fictional means to prove some spiritual point. How can we consistently select some people or events as actual and relegate others to a fictional role without prejudging? The historical accuracy of the scriptures follows from the character of the revelation itself, a true, holy God showing Himself in an historical context. Of course, the Bible *does* use literary devices: Christ did speak (often) in parables; metaphors and culturally-based expressions abound. One needs to recognize these facts in any interpretation of the teachings of scripture. The consistent Christian accepts the general and detailed *historical statements* and the Bible's own comments on them as good history, designed to show us how to be in a right relation with God. "He hath showed thee, O man, what is good; and what doth the Lord require of thee but to do

justly, and to love mercy, and to walk humbly with thy God"
(Mic. 6:8).

2. *The Biblical Text*

(a) "Critical" Theories

The traditional view of the writing of the Biblical texts is
that they were originally composed by authors roughly contemporary with the events. Moses compiled and wrote most
of the first five books, the Pentateuch; Samuel recorded the
events of Judges and the early kingdoms of Saul and David.
The prophets wrote the books called by their respective
names, as did the New Testament evangelists and apostles.

With the so-called "age of enlightenment," including the
eighteenth- and nineteenth-century development of scientific
methods and the humanistic philosophies that adopted science
as though it were theirs, there came a change in attitude
toward the Biblical text. The "rational" philosophy of the
1700's and 1800's formed a new basis for interpreting the
data then available. These data were meager, consisting
essentially of various late texts, codices, a few early manuscripts, writings of church fathers, rabbinical commentary,
and some secular historical documents. During the 1800's,
archaeological discoveries in the Middle East and Egypt
began dimly to shed light on the history and writings of the
Bible.

The theory of the Old Testament which was rife at the beginning of the twentieth century was that of the Graf-Keunen-
Wellhausen school, whose most influential exponent in English
was S. R. Driver. Briefly, it was held that there were several
documents and/or primitive orally transmitted and legendary
accounts of the creation, flood, patriarchs, the Israelite sojourn
in Egypt, the exodus, and the pre-kingdom days in Israel. For
instance, the first three chapters of Genesis are thought to be
based on at least two such documents, one of which (E)
used the name "Elohim" for God, the other (J) using the

name "Jehovah," or JAVH, for God. The stories in Genesis, Exodus, and Numbers were presumably legends in the time of David and Solomon, who themselves were tribal kings of little importance. As time went on and literacy increased, these histories were written down, and edited, until at the time of Josiah (circa 600 B.C.) an imaginative priest produced a document purporting to be the last injunctions of Moses, now known as Deuteronomy. Later, at the time of return of the Babylonian exiles, another free editing, presumably by Ezra, brought much of the Old Testament into something like its present text. Still later, writings of various prophets were added, and stories designed to inculcate patriotism or faith were included, such as those of Daniel and some of the Psalms.

Scholarly point-by-point analyses of this "documentary hypothesis" are given in the references cited, and so need not be made here.[3] These ideas of late editing and composition of the Bible run into a number of serious logical and experimental snags. Rutgers' Professor Yamauchi has pointed out the logical inconsistencies of the "double standard" used by literary critics, which has led to abandonment of a documentary theory in Homeric studies, but which continues the old theory of the Bible in the face of modern Biblical archaeological data.[4] The observed coincidences of accuracy concerning early Egypt, Palestine, the lands, customs, and artifacts, are too numerous to be the result of late forgeries. It is simpler to assume that the narratives of the Pentateuch are substantially Mosaic, and that Moses used, besides oral traditions, older documents written by various authors, some Egyptian, some family annals perhaps dating from the time

[3] See A. R. Short, *Modern Discovery and the Bible* (1952), pp. 159-178, for enlarged discussion; in the following, this reference will be cited as *MDB*. See also E. J. Young, *Introduction to Old Testament* (1950), for fuller treatment of the Hebrew text and W. J. Martin, *Stylistic Criteria and the Analysis of the Pentateuch* (1955); see also references given in Chapter VII.

[4] *Christianity Today*, Nov. 19, 1965, pp. 3-6.

of Abraham. This working assumption would account for the detailed historical accuracies found in the Pentateuch. Consistent with the physical evidence, then, is the assumption that God guided the original writers and any subsequent editors in the selection and recording of these narratives and the internal commentary made on them.

What we wish to emphasize is that the documentary hypothesis, sometimes called "higher criticism," rests on data which was the best available in the late 1800's. Modern Biblical archaeological data are generally embarrassing to this old theory. In an interesting article[5] entitled "Is Glueck's Aim to Prove that the Bible is True?" G. E. Wright points out that most Palestinian archaeological research has been carried out by non-fundamentalists, and that the towering authority of W. F. Albright is behind the statement that archaeology confirms Biblical history. Further, Albright (in *From the Stone Age to Christianity*) has "led the attack in the English-speaking world on the unexamined presuppositions of 'Wellhausenism' from the standpoint of ancient history and particularly archaeology."[6]

But it is to Wellhausen and Driver that many of the modern-day theologians owe their views of the Bible. It is this view, now rendered inconsistent with many of the facts, which underlies much of the modern-day humanistic neglect of the Bible. Many people in and out of organized Christian-

---

[5] *BAR*, p. 14.

[6] A good article by Dr. Harry Orlinsky, who is one of the foremost Hebrew scholars today, entitled "The Textual Criticism of the Old Testament" in *The Bible and the Ancient Near East* (1965), pp. 140-169, analyzes the state of modern literary criticism in terms of archaeological data. Albright's treatment of certain data is said to be "a tour-de-force that has gone a long way toward helping to disprove the opinion of Wellhausen and others that the list [of Levitic towns in Joshua 21 and I Chronicles 6] was essentially unhistorical from the very beginning." He goes on, "Considerable advance has been made in the textual criticism of the Hebrew Bible as a result of the discovery and sober analysis of the proto-Hebrew Ugaritic texts, along with [other data]. These documents have enabled the student . . . to respect . . . the integrity [of the Masoretic text]."

ity still uncritically accept the older documentary theory or one of the other "critical theories" which it has spawned.[7] Philosophically based on antisupernaturalism rather than scientifically based on archaeological discovery, these theories are used as a means of disbelief. We must hasten to add that the currently available data do not "prove" an evangelical, historic, Christian position to be true, except in the sense that one can account for the data consistently. Even if we possessed undoubted autographed manuscripts for the whole Bible, we would not have a proof that this set of books was God's revelation to man, since this is one of our inherently unprovable presuppositions. Conversely, even if God's processes of inspiration involved late editing of earlier texts and oral traditions, and this could be conclusively shown, the resulting literature is still consistently acceptable as God's revelation. We still have "to walk by faith" in the sphere of spiritual reality, no matter how much or how good the physically real data are.

(b) Archaeological Data Bearing on the Text

Before leaving the discussion of "higher criticism" and the origins of the Biblical text, let us examine some of the facts and artifacts we have been calling in as witnesses. Those we now briefly cite are introduced in the interest of showing that traditional early dates of origin and authorship are reasonable.

(1) A. R. Short[8] cites a number of facts which challenge the pre-archaeological, "critical" theories of the origins of the Old Testament. For example,

> The beginning of the Iron Age is usually given as 1200 B.C., and the first mention of iron in the Bible (Deut. 3:11, Josh.

[7] See the review of the English translation of Bultmann's book *History of the Synoptic Tradition* (1963) in *Christianity Today*, April 10, 1964, p. 651, for a discussion of form-criticism, and examples of the circular reasoning which characterize it.

[8] *MDB*, Chap. IX, p. 179.

17:16) was supposed to be too early to be true. We now know that it was used, though sparingly, as far back as 1400 B.C. . . . Iron objects were found in Tutankhamen's tomb. . . .

It is interesting to note that the first mention of metal in Genesis is of bronze or "copper," a very ancient reference. We know that the Bronze Age followed the Stone Age and was in turn followed by the Iron Age. A late editor or author, say in 1000 to 1500 B.C. could not have known this. In this detail, too, the Biblical reference appears to be accurate, and points to early recorded history.

(2) Much scholarly furor has been raised over the book of Daniel, since before 1880 the only non-Biblical sources for this period were Xenophon and Herodotus, whose histories ignore Belshazzar. Archaeological discovery has since provided many details which corroborate and complement the Biblical story of Daniel. Daniel was made "third in the kingdom" (Dan. 5:29), after Nabonidus and Belshazzar, although at the time (the eve of the Medo-Persian capture of Babylon) Nabonidus was a prisoner of war. Dr. Dougherty, Professor of Assyrian at Yale University, in his book *Nebuchadnezzar and Belshazzar* (1929) ranks, for historical accuracy, the fifth chapter of Daniel next to cuneiform literature.[9]

The book of Daniel, in the original, uses a number of Aramaic, Persian, and Greek words.[10] Driver interprets this to mean a date of composition after the conquest of Palestine by Alexander the Great (332 B.C.), instead of the traditional purported date between 600 and 535 B.C. The raw data are as follows: the Greek words in Daniel are names of musical instruments; and there was considerable artistic intercourse between the Eastern Oriental culture and the Greek Ionic period, long before Alexander. (It is as though the existence of German-English cognate words would be a proof to thir-

[9] *MDB*, p. 196.
[10] For more detail, see Wick Broomall, *Biblical Criticism* (1957), p. 252.

tieth-century historians, reconstructing our own times after the radioactive fallout has died away, that Germany had won World War I.) The fact that *only three* Greek words are used is better evidence for an early pre-Alexandrian date.

The Aramaic words in Daniel were shown to be consistent with Persian Empire usages by the discovery of the "Elephantine Papyri," a group of manuscripts found in Egypt in 1903.[11] Aramaic is shown to have been the language of diplomacy and trade throughout western Asia in the Persian period. By the time of the Greek Septuagint translation, or the later "critical theory" date of composition, many of the Aramaic words in Daniel were obsolete.

The history of Daniel is apparently accurate, and the literrary usages are consistent with the early authorship, so why do many scholars still cling to late, Maccabean, dates? Even the 1961 *Encyclopedia Americana* asserts that the book of Daniel was written by a pious Jew in 166-165 B.C. in an attempt to encourage his contemporaries in their struggle for survival. This conclusion apparently arises because Daniel predicts some events which seem to have occurred during the Seleucid period, rather specifically referring to Antiochus Epiphanes (Dan. 11:31-33). If these purported prophecies of Daniel were recorded in the fifth century B.C., whereas the break-up of the Persian, Greek, and Roman empires (Dan. 2:28-45) and the predicted desecration of the temple, occurred centuries later, then these prophecies are remarkable indeed. A person who presupposes that such prophecy is impossible will, of course, reject supernatural influences in the Bible, and will seek to interpret all the data in naturalistic terms. The point here is that this rather common, naturalistic, non-Christian interpretation of the historical and textual data is based on an *assumed* naturalistic, non-Christian world view. These same data — the accurate detailed history of the Persian conquest of Babylon, details not known apparently to Greek historians

[11] J. Finegan, *Light from the Ancient Past* (1946), p. 24.

of a century or so later, the statements of the text, the predicted Maccabean period history — all are equally (or more)
consistently interpretable in terms of an assumed historic and
supernaturalistic Christian world view.[12]

(3) Another interesting data-example is the ancient narrative of Sodom and Gomorrah. It seems clear that these "cities
of the plain" are now submerged under the Dead Sea, so we
may never be able to excavate them. But many ancient
historians[13] report that there were bitumen, or asphalt, seep-
ages in the area; and sulfurous, tarnishing odors in the area
around the Dead Sea plains.

Earthquakes are common in this rift-valley, and it is entirely possible that a destructive fire could have been touched
off by ignition of the gases and asphalt in the area. According
to a geologist quoted in the cited article,

> . . . The seepages, catching fire from lightning or human
> action, would adequately account for recorded phenomena
> without necessarily having recourse to supernatural or fanci-
> ful theories. . . .

The bias shows clearly in this quotation, and the confusion
of fact with interpretation. Actually, the historical and physical data available are mutually consistent. These data include
the Genesis account and the present scientific understanding
of the geology of the region. The supernatural elements of the
story are connected with the Biblical commentary rather than
with the description of what happened. Sodom and Gomorrah
were wicked cities. They were destroyed by a holy God, who
used the natural phenomena of His physical universe for the
purpose. (Possibly the destruction was effected deliberately
in such a way as to demonstrate the truth that an unbeliever
can account for the data without resorting to the supernatural,
if he so chooses. God does not owe it to us to prove Himself

[12] For a fuller treatment of fulfillment of Biblical prophecy, see B.
Ramm, *Protestant Christian Evidences* (1953), Chapter III.
[13] J. Penrose Harland, "Sodom and Gomorrah," *BAR*, p. 69.

on our terms.) The divine intervention at Sodom was to be a sign, to all for all time who are willing to receive it, of the judgment of God upon rebellious and incorrigibly wicked creatures. That it happened at just that time, and Abraham's and Lot's relation to the event, comprise the divine element. That it happened through the agency of certain physical or chemical processes in no way detracts from the supernatural aspect of the event.

At least one other theory has been propounded (in a Sunday newspaper supplement) concerning Sodom and Gomorrah. A Russian scientist has speculated that these towns were the dumping site for the atomic weapons of some extraterrestrial beings. This theory, at least, is open to experimental check, for it should be possible to analyze the isotopic ratios of bottom material from the Dead Sea to determine whether there are any neutron-rich isotopes or fission product residues there. To date no one has taken this theory seriously enough to check it. We mention it simply to show how far-fetched some will become in their attempt to avoid the implications of a divinely inspired revelation of God in the Bible. It is immediately obvious to the reader who has comprehended the argument here that even if Martians had bombed Sodom, and we know of it from some science-fictional time-machine observations, the Biblical account would not be thereby disproved, nor the divine character of the revelation one whit tarnished. *God can and does use His creation in His ways of intervening in and interacting with history.*

(4) P. E. Cleator,[14] in *Lost Languages,* illustrates the tendency of a science writer to intrude his philosophy or beliefs into his data interpretation, and to assert that because he can account for some data, his explanation is thereby proved correct. The book contains some interesting data on Semitic, Egyptian, and other ancient languages. It also contains, mixed among the data like Ruth amid the alien corn, a number of

[14] P. E. Cleator, *Lost Languages* (1962).

his own personal value judgments concerning the Hebrew literature (Old Testament), laws, and customs, mostly to the effect that the Israelites plagiarized existing or previous cultures. Specifically on this point, Cleator states that (1) Mosaic law should not be considered inspired since it appears to borrow extensively from the Code of Hammurabi (p. 112); (2) Hebraic monotheism, modes of worship, and early Biblical references to God ("El") are borrowed from previous Ugaritic (West Canaanite) concepts, and therefore should not be considered as revealed (p. 144); (3) other Genesis narratives are unreliable since they are similar to, and therefore must be based on, Babylonian stories such as the Gilgamesh Epic; (4) that there is no satisfactory resolution of the philosophical problem of evil in a world supposedly ruled by a good God. (See Section III.B.2.)

In these comments, of course, he makes the unwarranted leap from fact to philosophy. Linguistic or literary similarities do exist between the various texts he cites. If we begin by assuming, as Cleator apparently (but tacitly) does, that the Bible is no more than an ancient Hebrew anthology, then it is consistent to interpret these similarities in terms of plagiarism. But the similarities, even the word-for-word quotations in places, do not prove this charge. Much less do they prove that the Bible is uninspired or in error as many people (including P. E. Cleator) for their own reasons seem to want to believe. These linguistic data, as all scientific data, are philosophically neutral. If we assume that there is a God, that He has revealed Himself, and that the Bible records that revelation, then these similarities are no less easy to account for consistently than on the opposite view. The early human experiences with God, predating Sumerians, Babylonians, Canaanite (Ugaritic) peoples, and Hebrews, were a common legacy of tradition in the Fertile Crescent. These traditions naturally found their way into the literature of all the early people. God used Moses (and others) to record those parts of the narrative He desired to reveal as inspired. A reading of the actual words of the Gilgamesh Epic or the Ugaritic texts, or the Code of Hammurabi (as opposed to a reading of comments on them by someone whose naturalist philosophy requires him to put them on the same literary level as the Bible) is recommended.[15] Contrasting these other writings with the similar Biblical passages in Genesis will illuminate the Christian assumption that the Biblical record is inspired.

(5) Only one other technical historical Biblical example will be given here using the comprehensive Christian view as the means of interpretation, and this too must be only a brief introduction to a vast topic. The Dead Sea Scrolls have received much attention in both the popular and the scholarly press, and the raw data are still being accumulated. The reader is referred to W. S. LaSor's book and its bibliography for further discussion.[16]

The Dead Sea Scrolls were found in caves near an ancient site (Qumran), known to have been occupied for a time by a zealous Jewish cult. Coins, inscribed and datable from 136 B.C. to 135 A.D., were found at the site, which included a "monastery" and a cemetery. The most importance has been

15 George A. Barton, "The Code of Hammurabi and the Pentateuch," *Archaeology and the Bible* (1936), Part II, Chapter XIII, p. 378. In the same book, see Chapter XXIII, "Psalms from Babylonia and Egypt," especially pp. 502-505 for a comparison of Psalm 104 with the "Hymn to Aton" by Ikhnaton (Amenophis IV, the Pharaoh who ruled 1364-1347 and attempted to establish monotheism in sun worship). This comparison is interesting in the light of Cleator's flat statement that the Egyptian hymn was included in the compilation by the psalmist, an accusation that an unwary reader is likely to have to accept unless he can lay his hands on the raw data. (Note the need to apply the scientific method of separating data from their interpretation in one's reading habits.) Aside from two ejaculatory phrases in Ikhnaton's hymn in praise of the deity, there is essentially no similarity and many striking differences in concept and feeling. E.g., Ikhnaton considers darkness evil whereas the psalmist, whoever he may be or whatever his literary sources, in inspired praise recognizes night as another manifestation of God's mercy (vv. 19-20). No further comment is needed for the honest student who will take the trouble to get at the raw data for himself.
16 W. S. LaSor, *Amazing Dead Sea Scrolls* (1956); revised as *Dead Sea Scrolls and the Christian Faith* (1962).

attached to the many manuscripts and fragments found, containing whole texts of most of the Old Testament and Apocrypha, as well as lengthy interpretations, liturgy, and rules for the community. Linen cloth wrappings for these scrolls were dated by radiocarbon at 33 A.D., plus or minus 200 years. The site, apparently destroyed by the Romans in 68 or 69 A.D., was occupied more or less continuously by the religious sect now called the Qumran community beginning about 170 B.C.

There are indications that the Qumran people were a branch of the puritanical Essene sect, but this has not been conclusively proved. It has been speculated that John the Baptist was an Essene, perhaps even a Qumran initiate early in his career, but this assertion rests on circumstantial evidence at best, and many differences in the basic concepts exist between John and the Qumran cult. Even wilder speculations have seen the printers' ink tracing Christian origins to Qumran or Essene teachings, but the facts do not seem to support this conclusion. Certainly the early Christians knew of Essene groups, and these two movements shared an antipathy toward the Jewish Sanhedrin, but the Essene influence on Christian origins must have been slight in view of the many fundamental doctrinal, organizational, and conceptual differences. The similarities between the two groups are understandable because both recognized but rejected the Jerusalem Sadducees' politico-religious control. The dissimilarities are striking, in baptismal concepts, communal property rules, communal meal symbolism, attitudes toward Jewish law and eschatology, ethical and ascetic manifestations of faith, in missionary vision, and in initiatory rites and requirements.[17] The Qumran people had the scriptures and honored them; it is not surprising that they would have some beliefs in common with the Christians, who also accepted these scriptures as revealed of God.

Thus when appeal is made to the raw data, the Qumran

[17] LaSor, *Amazing Dead Sea Scrolls,* Chapter XVI, pp. 217ff.

literature is readily interpreted as having little direct bearing on the origins of Christianity, although some scholars, for philosophical reasons, tend to interpret the data as though it had.[18] However, the data from Qumran shed much light on the history and culture of its time, including the time of Jesus Christ and the apostles. Further, the new manuscripts have confirmed the unity and integrity of the Old Testament, and the carefulness of preservation of the text. Most of these Biblical manuscripts predate the Christian era, and read essentially the same as both the Hebrew (Masoretic) text of the tenth century A.D., and the Septuagint translation of circa 200 B.C. As far as the Biblical text is concerned, the discovery of the Dead Sea Scrolls has not only pushed back the dates of our earliest manuscripts, but has shown that by 100 B.C. the Old Testament in its traditional form was accepted as God's word. Since it takes time for traditions to jell, this speaks for the conservative, orthodox, historic Christian view of scripture.

There are enough similarities between Qumran ritual and doctrine and that of the early church to be suggestive. There are enough differences to warn us not to jump to too hasty a conclusion about connections between the two groups.

(6) Since F. F. Bruce's excellent little book *Are the New Testament Documents Reliable?* is still in print, the reader interested in this problem is referred there for the detailed discussion and further bibliography we have no space for here.

3. *Principles of Interpretation*

(a) Inspiration

A Christian view of inspiration that accounts for all the physical and scriptural data is, briefly, that God has worked in and through various men throughout history in more or less overt ways, and both with and without their knowledge

[18] J. M. Allegro, *The Dead Sea Scrolls* (1956).

of His working, to *record the words and concepts He wanted to use to reveal Himself to us.* God guided in the selection of historical data from current events or available records of previous events. God guided in the choice of words, normally using the vocabulary and mentality of a local prescientific cultural context to express or exemplify concepts with universal meaning which could later be seen to have validity for other cultures.

The data of archaeology,[19] and of the Biblical text itself, evidence a development of religious understanding from before the time of Abraham and on. When God spoke at any particular time, it was to show Himself or His will in a more extensive way than He had done previously. Abraham's concept of God was probably not as theologically lofty as Moses', nor as ours today. But God did not change. Christ incarnated the God of Adam, of Noah, of Abraham, of Jacob, of Moses, of David, of Isaiah, of Jeremiah, of Daniel, and of Ezra. He who spoke in earlier days through prophets has now spoken most fully through His Son. The understanding of the ancients concerning the revealed character of God was perhaps imperfect and incomplete, but the revelation itself was always accurate as far as it went. The process of revelation culminated in Christ, and is now limited only by the finitude of the physical world in which the Incarnation transpired, for in Him, i.e., in Christ, "dwelleth all the fullness of the God head (Deity) bodily." He who sees Jesus Christ has seen the Father.

Throughout the long unfolding of the knowledge of God, there has been a continuity, a unity of revelation engendered by the oneness of the God who was revealing Himself. The internal consistency of the written records bespeaks a self-consistent God who reveals Himself. The inspiration of the written record is concomitant with the fact that it is God who was and is revealing Himself. These records, because

[19] Cf. W. F. Albright, *From the Stone Age to Christianity* (1957).

they are an integral part of the total revelation of God in Christ, were inspired. God by His Spirit kept the frail and finite human writers from error, guiding (but usually not dictating) even in the choice of words as they recorded the progressive revelation.

These remarks regarding God's active intervention with the human authors apply also to the editors and others who played a part in transmitting the revelation down through history. We have cited some evidence to support a conservative, traditional, view of scriptural origins and transmittal. It is consistent with all the data to believe that there has been some editing of earlier records, and rescension of documents in the formation of the text. It apparently did not take place strictly according to the Wellhausen, Driver, or more modern form-critical theories, and we say this on scientific rather than philosophical grounds. It is consistent with all the data to include as perhaps unwitting recipients of God's guidance those men who decided on canonical questions, and textual editors, along with the original authors. The result is an integrated whole: the Bible is the record of God's revelation.

(b) Interpretation

The historicity and the inspiration of the Bible imply certain principles and precautions in interpretation. First, we must look for the way God is revealing Himself in the scriptural passage, and how it relates to the full revelation. That is, there are broad outlines in scriptural truth of which the student ought to be aware, lest he confuse side issues and details. In this connection remember that God's purposes in revelation are not to give man a complete scientific treatise on cosmology, zoology, or history. This implies also that tentativeness is another important principle of interpretation, since we may yet have acquired neither the broad view of scripture nor the complete detailed scientific understanding needed to harmonize the data.

Next, the fact that God guided writers in the details

should lead us to examine the precise wordings closely, and
in this sense to interpret literally. Note that a literal interpretation is not opposed to a symbolic, allegorical, or meta-
phorical one. The Bible *is* literature but with a purpose — to
show God to us in various aspects with which we can interact
with Him personally. As literature, the Bible uses literary
devices. Even words are symbols, so that in a very basic
semantic sense all interpretation is symbolic. However, the
word pictures God has caused to be painted of Himself in the
Bible are more than mere literary devices. The words themselves are important, having been, as we assume, inspired and
being clues to deeper truths concerning God's nature.

Third, the fact that inspiration operated with prescientific
cultural vocabulary and concepts should alert us to the possible need for parabolic interpretation, and for seeking the
transcultural elements in the record. Some incidents and narratives recorded in the Bible are explicitly stated to be acted
parables or physical illustrations of spiritual truths. It is thus
consistent to assign this type of meaning to other passages
of the Bible when it does not lead to contradictions and when
it allows a more "natural" total interpretation. (Note that
this is an interpretive principle used in the Bible itself.)
Further, there are early scriptural passages, referred to at
later points in the Biblical revelation, that are said to be
written for the learning of later generations, including our own
modern one. It is flatly stated (in an epistle of Peter) that
the original writers, the prophets, did not understand fully
what was being revealed through them (concerning at least
one major doctrine[20]). Therefore, we have not only the
privilege but the responsibility to seek the fuller meanings of
the Bible as they may be understood, with God's help, in our
modern scientific cultural context. We are definitely not to
be limited to interpreting a passage only as the original
writer might have conceived its meaning and application to

[20] II Peter 1:20-21.

life within *his* own cultural framework. We are to seek those revealed aspects of God's nature and relationship to His creation that transcend human cultures and languages, that are, so to speak, invariant.

Underlying all these principles of Biblical interpretation is the ground rule the Bible itself lays down — our need to depend upon God for enlightenment. The same Spirit who guided the original writers and editors makes Himself available to guide the modern reader who is willing to act upon what he reads. Intellectual or academic curiosity is not enough, but the whole person is to be involved, honestly, and humbly. Then the Spirit of the eternal Father makes use of these other principles, as one might use various brushes in painting a picture, to give literal details, or symbolic or summary broad brush treatment of the scriptural data in His development of our individual understanding of Himself.

These interpretation principles will be illustrated in what follows.

(c) Demythologizing the Bible

What we have said here about Biblical interpretation contrasts sharply with what many modern theologians call "demythologizing" the scriptures. It is a laudable and plausible aim to understand the revelation of God in meaningful modern cultural terms. This is — or should be — the object of all homiletic discourse. However, the current trend in Protestantism, following the lead of Bultmann and Tillich, is to reinterpret the Biblical words and symbols into "nonsymbolic" abstractions rather than into vital relationships with God.[21] The Biblical terms that might be offensive to the modern mind are made palatable by redefinition. As K. Runia puts it, "The theologian masters God's word and makes it say what he thinks. The words of the Bible are no longer allowed to

[21] Klaas Runia, *I Believe in God* . . . (1963), p. 60.

have their own meaning, but are first emptied of their original meaning and then refilled with the philosophical presuppositions of man. . . ." This is Gnosticism. Actually, the symbols of Christianity bespeak realities too far beyond finite human understanding for any nonsymbolic interpretation. What Tillich and others do then, in effect, is not to demythologize the Bible but rather to *remythologize* it into current humanistic symbols. In doing so, they "reject the concepts selected by the Bible, i.e., by God Himself, to communicate to us the reality of His Being and of His creative and redemptive activity, and replace them by quite different concepts." [As a consequence] "the reality expressed by them is also quite different."[22] Deity so expressed is not the eternal, supernatural, personal, Biblical God revealing Himself, but it is a finitely understood result of a humanist assumption about God. Thus there is enough vagueness in Tillich's God, the abstract "ground-of-being," to allow a man to avoid personality involvement and, as a necessary consequence, to preclude personality fulfillment. There is little in these abstract humanistic notions to help a person acquire either a satisfying relationship with God or the personal morality needed for adequate relationships with other men.

All scripture, as all data, needs interpretation within the integrating framework of some view. If that view is humanism or naturalism, it is not thereby more "scientific" than evangelical Christianity or any other theistic view. It is patently possible to frame a humanistic world view that interprets both observed facts and Biblical statements; one simply rejects the Biblical statements with which he doesn't wish to agree. It is possible also to redefine the meanings of Biblical concepts so as effectively to reject them. In this case one should recognize that he is building a humanist view and not a Christian one. Hence, the interpretations placed on all data will be within the humanist framework rather than a

[22] Runia, *op. cit.*, p. 62.

Christian one, no matter what it may be called by its adherents.

A true Christian interpretation of scriptural symbolism will be characterized by the principles elicited in the last section. The Christian view recognizes prescientific language and ancient cultural contexts as such, and symbolic or literary language. For example, we do not hold dogmatically that "heaven" is a physical place, "up" in the sky somewhere, occupying physical space and constituted of atoms and molecules.[23] Perhaps the ancient writers did, but the revelation of God to modern man is not assisted by this concept, and the language of scripture bearing on this point is interpretable as of a reality too wonderful to be contained in the notions of mere four-dimensional space-time. The Christian interpretation is thus one that accepts (by faith) the reality being symbolized. In contrast, the humanistic "nonsymbolic" interpretation would dismiss the concept of heaven as myth, and therefore as unworthy of the concern of modern man at all. It throws out the baby with the bath. Such "demythologizing" is clearly contrary to the Spirit of revelation, who desires to operate today among us scientific moderns, if only we are willing to open our minds to the breadth, depth, and scope of the revelation.

4. Conclusion

The few examples cited so far serve to illuminate the principle that physical data are philosophically neutral. The physically observable objective data of the Bible itself, of the Middle Eastern archaeology, and other pertinent historical data may, on close inspection, be found to be consistent with

[23] Although the Bishop of Woolsey, Dr. J. A. T. Robinson, in *Honest to God,* alleges that we do. See the critical article "The New Theologian I. Ecce Homo" on the so-called "New Morality" and Dr. Robinson in *The New Yorker* magazine, Nov. 13, 1965, p. 63. See also, "A Reply to the God-Is-Dead Mavericks" by Carl F. H. Henry, *Christianity Today,* May 27, 1966, p. 33.

the Christian assumptions. That is, the raw data can be
interpreted in terms of belief that God has caused to be therein recorded His revelation of Himself to mankind. There are
those who make naturalistic assumptions the basis for interpretation of these same physical data. We Christians feel
that such an interpretation has difficulty accounting for the
detailed historical accuracy and other matters cited here.[24]
In every case we have analyzed we have found that the only
difficulty involved in consistent Christian interpretation was
in getting at the raw data. Most often the data presented by
the non-Christian as excuse for disbelief in the Bible is "processed" data, that is, raw data already partly interpreted on
the basis of his assumed non-Christian philosophy. When we
critically study the problems of interpreting the physical
data, we find that the basic facts in each case can be reinterpreted consistently by the Christian.

All anyone should ask (intellectually) of his assumed world
view is that it enable him to interpret his data consistently.
The Christian's faith is not blind but it is faith. However, it
is not primarily intended as a means of interpreting the
physical data of Biblical history. Rather, it is a means of
spiritual understanding and acquiring a proper relationship to
God. It is our purpose here to discuss mainly the scientific,
i.e., physical, problems of the Christian view. These problems are solvable satisfactorily, i.e., with intellectual honesty,
within the Christian world view.

B. ORIGINS

1. *Cosmogony — The Origin of the Universe*

(a) The Physical Data and Theories to Account for Them

There is a tremendous amount of information gathered over
the centuries that relates to the universe as a whole, to our
galaxy, and to our solar system in particular. Those cosmologi-

---

[24] That is, without making more *ad hoc* assumptions.

cal data include: (1) the "red shift," the slight increase in wave length of light observed in faraway stars, with more change the more distant (apparently) the star; (2) the existence of galaxies, their forms (spiral, elliptical or other) or lack of form (irregular), and the distribution of cosmic radio waves emitted by hydrogen gas (21-cm. wave length) from both stars and galaxies; (3) the abundance of elements and the ratios of various isotopes, as determined spectroscopically in the light from the stars; (4) the apparent applicability of much of Einstein's Special and General Relativity Theory in description of cosmological processes,[25] as judged from several crucial verification experiments. Many more data are available to the interested student, relating to the formation of galaxies and individual stars. These data include observations on such diverse entities as optically dark gas clouds in space, stellar temperatures and sizes, and thermonuclear reaction details.

Despite the large amount of astrophysical data, as yet one is not led conclusively to a unique description of the origins of the universe. At the present time there are three theories of the universe that seriously attempt to account for the available astrophysical data.

One, the evolutionary or "big bang" theory, supposes that at some time in the distant past, perhaps ten to fifteen billion years ago, the universe began from a small volume.[26] Variations of the theory suppose that this energy was electromagnetic (light waves), or particles of matter (neutrons), but in any case its energy density, and matter density, was enormous. This primordial material expanded, elements were formed by known nuclear reactions, and the universe developed. The "red shift" is interpreted in terms of universal

[25] See, for example and a bibliography, J. A. Wheeler, "Problems on the Frontiers between Relativity and Differential Geometry," *Reviews of Modern Physics,* Vol. 34 (October, 1962), pp. 873-892.

[26] Professor George Gamow is the most literary proponent of this theory. See *One, Two, Three . . . Infinity* (1960), for example.

expansion; that is, light from faraway stars and galaxies receding from us is seen with longer wave lengths because of the motion of the light sources, just as the pitch of a receding train whistle sounds lower than it would if the train and observer were not in relative motion. All the galaxies were presumably formed early in the history of the universe, but all need not have become luminous or condensed at the same time, so young irregular galaxies can be accounted for.

The second, or "steady state universe" theory has been eloquently expounded by Professor Fred Hoyle and has acquired a considerable number of adherents since it was introduced in the 1940's.[27] In order to avoid the physically (and mathematically) rather unpleasant situation of having essentially infinite density at zero time as required by the bang theory, this theory supposes that matter is uniformly dense in the universe and has always been so. Since the observed red shift implies that the universe is expanding, this uniform average density of matter is supposed to result from the continuous creation *ex nihilo* of matter in space. In other words, it is a property of space that matter — atomic hydrogen — is being continuously created to maintain an average density of about 0.000001 grams per cubic centimeter in the expanding universe. This newly created matter ultimately condenses into new galaxies. A prediction of this theory that has turned out to be difficult to verify by observation is that the galaxies should be uniformly distributed throughout the whole universe; the difficulty comes in counting the numbers of faraway galaxies and their distances with certainty. Hoyle admits that continuous creation of matter, even at the extremely slow rate required by the theory to fit the data, is a strange *ad hoc* hypothesis, but points out that this allows one to account for much data otherwise hard to explain, and many scientists feel it is no more strange than the evolutionary theory notion of an infinite density at the beginning.

[27] F. Hoyle, *The Nature of the Universe* (1955).

Recent developments in radioastronomy along with other data have caused some changes in Hoyle's scientific thinking that can be better discussed after considering the third main cosmological theory, the "oscillating universe." This theory may account more easily for the data than either of the other two.[28] Among the admissible solutions of the relativistic cosmological equations are several formulae for the radius of the universe. One of these formulae indicates that the size of the universe oscillates with a time period calculated at several tens of billions of years. That is, it is mathematically possible according to the modern solutions of Einstein's equations for the universe to have been concentrated in a smaller volume some ten to fifteen billion years ago, to be expanding now but slowing down in its expansion, until in another five to ten billion years the universe will be of maximum size and begin to decrease. The decrease in size will continue until everything is back at a minimum radius and then the whole expansion history of the universe will repeat. This process could have been going on for an infinite time, and can continue indefinitely, according to the equations. Thus, we now see an expanding universe similar to the one accounted for by the bang theory, but with the possibility of an infinitely long existence.

Although visible galaxy counting in the universe is difficult, counts of the known radio-frequency sources can be made. Assuming these radio sources are cosmological entities, their observed distribution appears more consistent with a universe having decreasing density (increasing size) than with a steady state uniform universe. This tentative interpretation of the 21-cm. wave length radio data, coupled with interpretation of (1) observed brightness distributions in

[28] A popular exposition has been given by Öpik in *The Oscillating Universe* (1960); and a readable, technical discussion is given by J. A. Wheeler in *International Journal of Science & Technology*, Dec. 1963. In addition to utilizing general relativity in cosmology, this theory allows a rather elegant geometrical description of electromagnetic phenomena, and has a lot of esoteric appeal to theoretical physicists.

elliptical galaxies, (2) observed 7-cm. wave length radio noise background data, and (3) observed helium-to-hydrogen ratios in nebulae and stars in our galaxy, has led Hoyle to propose a modification to the older steady state theory.[29] The new hypothesis, like the old one, is consistent within the framework of general relativity, and attributes to free space the ability to create matter *ex nihilo*. However, the new theory considers all that we can observe astronomically, and perhaps some more, to be an island universe, or "metagalaxy" in an infinite sea of space which contains other metagalaxies. (Alfven[30] considers the likely possibility that the metagalaxies contain matter and antimatter galaxies or stellar systems, and that the high intensity radio emissions observed in some regions of the sky are due to annihilation energy.) Hoyle theorizes that our own metagalaxy is full of galaxies and other objects and is oscillating in size. It is a "local" inhomogeneity in an infinite space, presently expanding; but at some future time, when gravitational forces overcome the expansion, contraction will begin. Because of the assumed properties of free space, the contraction will proceed to some minimum (metagalactic) radius, not zero; that is, the material density will become large but not infinite, and will again begin to decrease. Ultimately, according to this theory, the oscillations will "damp out," or reduce in amplitude until they cease. At that far future time, our region of the universe, the metagalaxy we know, will resume a steady state existence with uniform matter density. There will be no galaxies in it but only the thin gas of space. However, elsewhere in the infinite sea of metagalaxies there will arise other oscillatory inhomogeneities in density, that is, other metagalaxies. Thus Hoyle has postulated an infinite and eternal material universe that is consistent with the observable data so far obtained.

[29] F. Hoyle, "Recent Developments in Cosmology," *Nature*, Vol. 208 (October 9, 1965), p. 111.

[30] H. Alfven, "Antimatter and the Development of the Metagalaxy," *Reviews of Modern Physics*, Vol. 37 (October 1965), p. 652.

Note that one is out on a long, thin limb of philosophical speculation if he asserts that the material universe actually is eternal, even though the scientific equations do not *per se* preclude it. No conceivable observed data could prove such a conclusion. Further, (kinematic) equations of motion in physics commonly involve the time without any specification of when time began or when the situation described ceases to exist. (The equation of periodic wave motion is x (displacement) = a sine (bt), where a and b are constants. The equation itself tells us nothing about when the wave started to oscillate, nor when the vibration stops for any reason. Similarly the equations written to describe the expansion of the universe contain the parameter time, t, along with many other physical quantities, with no intrinsic means of specifying a beginning of time.) The equations allow one to describe a *theoretically* eternal situation where $-\infty < t < +\infty$ but the eternity is an artifact of the kinematical method of description, and need not be taken as an indication that the physical situation being described *actually* is eternal. The cosmological equations may equally well describe a universe which has a beginning in time and some specified boundary conditions. Thus the inference need not be drawn that the universe has had an infinite existence.

We shall not discuss these cosmological theories further, technically. The observed data can be generally explained by all three theories, although the current trend of belief is toward the oscillating universe description. To date, no completely definitive or crucial experiment has been done, nor are the inherent observational errors yet small enough, to decide uniquely which, if any, of the three is most correct.

(b) The Scriptural Data, and an Interpretation

One further source of cosmogonical data is available to the Christian: "In the beginning God created the Heavens and the Earth, and the Earth was without form and void." We need not read any preconceived cosmological model into these revealed statements; none is there intrinsically. It seems that God's purpose (in revealing this datum) is to let us know that He is the Creator of the universe. Apparently He didn't want to force the prescientific Hebrews to wade through some technical jargon on the astrophysical processes involved, since they might have stopped reading before they got to the really important parts of this record of His revelation of Himself.

The word "beginning," along with the past tense of the verb "created" used in Genesis 1:1 may seem to favor the evolutionary ("bang") theory of the universe, but these terms are equivocal. Ancient Hebrews used one form for all past tenses, so it is possible that a concept other than simple past-action-at-a-specific-time could be reasonably inferred. The word "beginning" is used of God Himself in John 1:1, "In the beginning was the word and the word was with God and the word was God. . . ." Compared with the concepts that God has "neither beginning nor end," and "I am Alpha and Omega, the beginning and end," it seems possible also to interpret Genesis 1:1 to mean that God has been creating the physical universe always. It may be a facet of God's infinite nature thus to interact in time, although He Himself exists independently of time. Space, time, and matter seem physically to be necessary concomitants, but eternity is related to the spiritual character of God. With these not unscriptural ideas in view, a Christian could accept a steady state or oscillating picture of the universe, if the observable data all turn out to be best interpretable in those terms. This would fit into an even grander concept of the nature of God than one would have had before beginning his study of cosmology.

In the phenomenology of scripture the creation of the heavens refers to the coming into existence of the visible heavens, primarily our galaxy, but possibly also including all observable galaxies in our metagalaxy (out to the inherent limit, a few times our present instrumental limit). All cosmologists, regardless of their philosophical views, grant that the observable stars and galaxies all had beginnings at some specific past times. Of course, the next phrase in Genesis 1:1 refers to the origin of the earth in the solar system, a much later event than the galactic origin. Keeping in mind the evidence for present-day condensation of galaxies out of optically transparent cosmic hydrogen gas, consider the statement of Hebrews 11:3, "Through faith we understand that the worlds were framed by the word of God, so that things which are seen were not made of things which do appear."

This will illustrate the frequent ambivalence of scriptural statements in matters of science. The revealed data apply primarily to our individual human relationships with God and one another. They neither intrinsically support nor preclude any of the current scientific (i.e., descriptive) hypotheses on the origins of the universe. Gamow, Hoyle, Alfven, or Öpik, or none of them, may be correct in his *scientific* views on origins of the universe; the correct interpretation of observed data will be found eventually to be consistent with the simple statements of Genesis.

Here is a classic example of the limitation of science to *describe* nature, leaving to one's philosophical views the problems of the ultimate meaning of that description. Unfortunately, some scientists writing on these cosmological theories are unwilling or unable to separate their scientific and philosophical notions. As we read the popular expositions we find often unwarranted extrapolations from science into matters of faith. (E.g., Hoyle, *op. cit.*, Chapter 7, in spite of its being labelled a "Personal View" could mislead an unwary reader; similarly Öpik, *op. cit.*, Chapter 1.) The Christian view says that however the universe began or has always been, or whatever its cosmology, God caused and causes it to be so. This view allows fully consistent interpretation of all physical data, and this is all one can ask any world view to do for these data.

2. Evolution — The Origin of Man

In a study of human origins not only is there a vast amount of data to be interpreted, but these facts come from such a wide range of scientific disciplines that a specialist in one field may have only a partial picture of the whole study. The geologist who estimates dates of a stratum normally cannot comment on the details of the anatomical articulation of the bones found in the stratum. The paleontologist, in turn, likely is not an authority on the geographical or ecological factors that favor one tendency in anatomical structure over another. Probably neither a geologist nor a zoologist would also be a geneticist who could experiment with rates at which mutations occur under various environments in various species with various mutagenic stimuli, such as radiation-induced free radicals, or thermal excitation of molecules. The geneticist, in turn, need not specialize in radiation physics, astrophysics, the biochemistry of proteins, nor in archaeology, ethnology, or anthropology. Yet each of these scientific fields studies phenomena that bear upon the description of human origins.

Further, the subject of human origins has been a battleground in a conflict of philosophies. Some Biblical statements are given us, and these have been usually interpreted without regard for the need for over-all consistency of all data — both scientific and scriptural. If a Christian offers a scientist no alternative but to ignore the plethora of physical evidence, then the Christian should not be surprised that the scientists of this age have chosen rather to ignore the scriptural data.[31] The true Christian view offers no such alternatives; it is not a matter of *either* the scriptures *or* scientific data, for when all truth is seen as God's, then one's mind is open to reinterpret *all* the available data. The result is no

---

[31] Conversely, if a biologist insists to all that his scientific description — evolution — supports naturalistic philosophy against a Christian view, then he should not be surprised to find Christians taking issue. A true scientist does not make this dogmatic extrapolation to philosophy, but recognizes the neutrality of descriptive science.

compromise between science and theology, but a working hypothesis that accounts consistently for the available data.

(a) Origin of Life

Much speculation exists in the literature of science on the origins of life on this planet. Astronomical data on atmospheres of other planets and comets, and on the theories of formation of sun-planet systems, have given us reason to think that the earth's primeval atmosphere was rich in hydrogen, methane, ammonia, and water vapor. In addition, ionizing radiation was present both from radioactive rocks and extraterrestrial sources such as solar and cosmic rays. It is tempting to try to simulate the postulated primeval environment of two to three billion years ago in the laboratory and to look for chemical reactions. Such experiments have been done and complex organic (carbonaceous) molecules have been formed. All this proves is that some of the building blocks for life processes could have been formed by the random encounters of molecules that probably existed in the virgin earth's atmosphere or seas.[32]

Among other data to be considered in a study of origins of life are recent advances in biochemistry, which have demon-

---

[32] For an interesting train of speculation, see C. Sagan, "On the Origin and Planetary Distribution of Life," *Radiation Research*, Vol. 15 (Aug. 1961), pp. 174-192. For a contrary opinion regarding the probability of random molecular collisions producing biochemical compounds and, eventually, living systems, see Lecompte du Noüy, *Road to Reason* (1949), who asserts that there has not been enough time for chemical statistics to account for the formation of living systems on earth. By way of commenting on du Noüy's argument, we must realize that there may be a large number of biochemical ways in which some form of life could have arisen, as well as the particular way in which it did arise to produce life as we know it. If this be so, then the probability of formation of a small virus, say, having a few thousand atoms is not proportional simply to $1 \div N$ where N is the number of chemically different ways one can rearrange the atoms. Instead it would be proportional to $M \div N$ where M is the number of biologically significant ways the atoms could be arranged to form a reproducing virus.

strated the complexity of the vital processes of cellular metabolism. For example, consider the respiration cycles by
which mitochondria replenish the adenosine triphoshate
(ATP) in cells, and the way in which cells use the phosphate
bond energy, converting ATP to adenosine diphosphate
(ADP). The mitochondrial structure, function and operation appear to be the *same for all species.* The enzymes that
guide these chemical cycles, and every other cellular chemical
reaction, are apparently formed in response to information
carried in genes in the cell. These genes, in turn, appear to
be ordered sets of chemical bases strung along a helical
desoxyribonucleic acid (DNA) molecule, and the ordering of
these bases constitutes the so-called "genetic code." Probably the most exciting scientific discovery presently in the making is the breaking (understanding) of the genetic code. These
remarks are highly oversimplified, but they indicate the chemical intricacy of a living system, data to be accounted for by
any theory of the origin of life.

The geological data bearing on the origin of life deal
principally with the time scales available. Dating of the
time of solidification of rocks by means of ratios of various
isotopes of uranium, thorium, lead, and potassium is an accepted technique, and leads to ages as old as several billion
years. In addition, the oldest rock strata in which we find
evidence for plant and animal life are datable as having been
laid down earlier than 600,000,000 years ago. These are Pre-
Cambrian algae, fungi, worm tracks, and other soft-bodied
animal impressions in mud found in sedimentary rock. The
algae and bacteria appear to be as old as two billion years.[33]
Animals such as worms represent complex organisms compared
to a single cell, which in turn is complex compared to the
virus-like, large replicating molecules thought to have been
the first "living" things. An abundance of fossil shells in

[33] See a series of articles on Pre-Cambrian algae in the Gunflint
Chert, *Science,* Vol. 147 (Feb. 5, 1965), pp. 563-577; Vol. 148 (April
2, 1965), pp. 27-35; and Vol. 149 (Sept. 17, 1965), pp. 1365-7.

Cambrian strata indicates ubiquitous marine life by a half-billion years ago. By a few hundred million years later, the strata indicate, land plants were well established; first insects, then amphibians, reptiles, and mammals seem to have flourished, in that order. The time scales, involving hundreds of millions of years, are almost beyond comprehension, and this fact probably contributes to the difficulty some people have accepting a statistical description of the origin of living materials.

Recently, a quite different line of speculation has arisen concerning the origin of life on earth. Several investigators have reported what appear to be spores or unusual algal forms in meteorites. The possibility is suggested that our primal life came from some such extraterrestrial source, from an established life pattern on another planet in another solar system. The facts are that the meteors in which these "organic" specks were found fell to earth long ago, and it is an equally likely scientific interpretation of these data that the spores found are the result of contamination from earthly life.[34]

The Biblical data comprise a few statements in early Genesis:

> And God said, let there be a firmament (expanse) in the midst of the waters and let it divide the waters from the waters. And God made the firmament, and divided the waters. And God called the firmament heaven; and the evening and the morning were the second day.
>
> And God said, let the waters under the heaven be gathered together in one place, and let the dry land appear and it was so. . . .
>
> And God said, let the earth bring forth grass, the herb yielding seed, and the fruit tree yielding fruit after its kind.
>
> And God said, let there be lights in the firmament of the heaven to divide the day from the night, the greater light to rule the day, and the lesser light to rule the night: He made the stars also to give light upon the earth. . . .

[34] E.g., see *Science*, June 7, 1963, p. 1097.

And God said, let the waters bring forth abundantly the moving creature that hath life, and fowl that may fly above the earth in the open firmament of heaven. . . .

These statements, as all data, need interpretation. The "days" are evidently periods of time, the Hebrew word "yom" being often so used elsewhere, and the words "morning" and "evening" then referring to a beginning and end of an era. The language is prescientific, but the order of events is striking, in view of the present belief that single-celled plant life (algae, etc.) was first on earth.[35] For several billion years before this, the chemical reactions in the thick atmosphere (firmament) and in the hot condensing seas could have produced a variety of possibly useful building blocks for life's physical processes. It is now thought that the atmosphere originated from the "outgassing" or release of absorbed and adsorbed gases from the hot primordial rock. During the course of millions of years of rain, the atmosphere would have begun to clear, allowing photosynthetically useful wave lengths to enter. The earth would be quite cool by then so that the atmospheric moisture would have been separate from the seas (as the Bible says), and dry land became possible. Then the more complex and efficient (because of photosynthesis) plants began to develop. As the atmosphere cleared further, the sun, moon, and stars appeared, having been created long before but obscured from the earth, as they are from Venus even today. The striking thing is that, while the language is phenomenological, the order of events in Genesis is close to that inferred by modern scientific speculation based on available data.

[35] For example, there are simple plants that can use atmospheric hydrogen and CO_2 to generate cellular carbohydrates without photosynthesis. In the thick early atmosphere, which absorbed most of the sun's light, such plants or their precursors could have flourished. Note that we are only speculating here with a possible description of events. It may be that the atmospheric hydrogen had already diffused away into space, and other biochemical processes were used to bring single-celled forms of life into being.

Science, of course, cannot say *why* these events occurred as they did; the Bible gives only a sketchy description of *how* they occurred, but does state that God caused these events to happen. The laws of chemistry and statistics are God's laws, so the processes are at once natural and supernatural. Science speculates that it could have happened as we have briefly outlined and the Biblical data are remarkably consistent with what physical facts there are.[36]

(b) Development of Higher Forms

Paleontology, geographical distributions of species, and comparative anatomy, to name but three fields of science, present an overwhelming mass of data to be interpreted. A salient feature is that the complexity of the animal forms in any past era is directly correlatable with the date of that era. Another striking fact is that various isolated regions of the earth have separate species of the same type of animal or plant, and that these species appear suited to the particular environment of their regions. Another class of data is the similarity in form and function of various cells and cell systems that are common to many different types of animals and plants, e.g., eyes, or mitochondria, or, even more basic, the similarity of the polynucleotide sequences (genetic code) in DNA of various species.[37] These scientific data and many more appear to be elegantly accounted for by a single unifying biological principle, the theory of evolution.

The evolutionary principle in biology asserts that new species can develop during the course of many generations in response to changes in the species' total environment. In a large population of some particular species, for instance, there are individuals with various traits and abilities, extra resistance to certain diseases, or ability to see better in the dark, to resist cold or heat, or move faster because of some bone struc-

36 Even an extraterrestrial spore-laden meteor is not precluded as the source of physical life by the raw data of the Bible.
37 *Science*, Vol. 104 (May 22, 1964), pp. 959-967.

ture. In the particular situations in which this population is located, certain of these traits are more important for survival, and so certain of these individuals have an advantage over the others. During succeeding generations, the proportion of those individuals that have the advantageous traits or abilities tends to increase in the population, relative to the others. After a very long time, it may be that the population is composed entirely of individuals with these traits.

A well-known contemporary example of this process is the development of new virus strains, such as those that cause recurrence of "flu" epidemics, or of drug-resistant strains of germs. For most staphylococcus bacteria pencillin is lethal, but for a few it is not. These resistant germ strains have become a larger fraction of the bacterial population in succeeding generations, as the other germs were killed off. This is a simplified summary of how "natural selection" operates, since normally many environmental factors are at work at once.

This principle explains the development of more complex forms in terms of their better adaptability or suitability to the changing environments of the earth, and equally well accounts for both the stability and changeability of species. It explains the observed different species in isolated regions in terms of survival of the fittest traits. It explains the similarity in form and function of organs in various animal types because these basic functional units, e.g., mitochondria, nerves, photoreceptors (eyes), etc., serve their parent organisms well in complex enough ways that probably no small changes in their design could assist them in doing jobs better, so no survival advantage would result from a small change in any given generation.

The mechanisms by which natural selection can operate have been elicited only recently in the science of genetics. We know now, by microscopic and biochemical observation, that every living cell has chromosomes and genes. The specific genes seem to determine specific characteristics of the living cell, and of the animal of which that cell is a part.[38] (The genes themselves are complex biochemical systems and the means by which the genes control enzyme production and cell functions is under intense study.) We know that chromosomes break and reform, that genes undergo "spontaneous" changes in structure — mutations — perhaps because of absorbed cosmic or terrestrial radiation or thermal agitation. Thus genes in living cells are continually exposed to influences by which they may be chemically modified. Within any species there are large numbers of contemporaneous members who look alike and differ only in subtle genetic ways. In a specific environment, the population of these strains that can function best will tend to build up. Thus genetics provides the method by which natural selection can operate.

The fact is that genetics is an observationally-based science, as well as one with deductive roots in biochemistry, biophysics, and mathematical statistics. The fact is that laboratory tests with many generations of *Drosophila melangoaster* (common fruit fly), and also other species, have shown that *most, but not all*, mutations are harmful. Other laboratory studies with simpler systems, bacteria with shorter generation times, have actually demonstrated new bacterial species by induced gene mutations and subsequent adaptation to environment.

The fact is that virtually every biologist accepts the principles of evolution as a means of consistently accounting for all the physical data indicated. Evolution is as well demonstrated a biological principle as any scientific principle can be. However, notice that it is a *scientific* principle, i.e., a *means of describing physical* phenomena and of accounting for physical data on the development of higher forms of life on earth. It is as unwarranted to make evolution a philosophical principle as it is to assert that physics supports determinism as a philosophy.

[38] An interesting summary of much current knowledge about cells is contained in the September 1961, *Scientific American*, a "symposium issue" devoted to "The Living Cell."

The Biblical data that bear on the physical aspects of the development of higher forms are mostly in Genesis: on the fifth "day,"

> God said, let the waters bring forth abundantly the moving creature that hath life and fowl that may fly above the earth . . . and God created great whales and every living creature that moveth which the waters brought forth abundantly, after their kind. . . .

> And God said, let the earth bring forth the living creature after his kind, cattle and creeping things, and beast of the earth after his kind. . . .

There is no discrepancy here. The biological principle of evolution describes the means by which God brought the living creatures forth from the seas and the land. The language is still prescientific and phenomenological and the order of events is strikingly close to that inferred by biologists from the existing physical data. A salient feature of genetic science is described in Genesis: the stability of species; but the absolute fixedness of species is not explicitly taught. The word "kind" might be interpreted to mean a broad classification, or the words "after his kind" might refer to a single generation's obvious similarity to its parents.

Some scientists feel that the laws of statistics preclude random chemical processes in the short space of two billion years as the means by which all these evolutionary changes took place. They invoke specific divine intervention at various times to account for the multiplicity and complexity of living forms. This theory of "special creation" of types or orders is acceptable, but may not be necessary as a means of accounting for the actual data. The Christian can believe that the laws of genetics, of kinetics, of biochemistry, and of natural selection are God's laws as surely as the more obvious law of gravity. Perhaps God intervened supernaturally at specific times, but even if it could be somehow conclusively shown by scientific methods that the development of complex living forms proceeded purely according to the statistical and evolutionary principles outlined (and accepted by most biologists), the faith of an understanding Christian would not be shaken, but could be rather strengthened. The raw data of scripture do not conflict with those of biology.

Certainly there is no excuse for rejection of God in the acceptance of the evolutionary theory as long as one is dealing with biology and describing the physical mechanisms of creation.

(c) The Development and Creation of Man

The fossil record that traces primate forms through the past seventy million years has many gaps. It is not as clear-cut a case of development as that of the horse, traceable with actual excavated bones from *eohippus* to *equus*. However, there is an increasing number of bones and skulls, being now dug out of various sites in Africa, and dated by isotope ratios in the rock in which they are imbedded. These data allow anatomists to deduce such things as gait and posture (from pelvic or back bones), or to inter-compare foreheads, crania, or mandibles on various skulls. Remains of human-type skeletons have been found widely distributed throughout the world — Java, China, Europe, as well as Africa. The earliest dated finds are those in Tanganyika's Olduvai Gorge, of *Zinjanthropus* and *Habilis*, who walked erect and apparently used sticks and stones as tools about a million years ago.[39] Few data yet have been discovered that shed light on

[39] See the various papers by L. S. B. Leakey in *Nature*. For a good descriptive, dispassionate review of the results from Olduvai Gorge, and a current bibliography, see P. V. Tobias, "Early Man in East Africa," *Science*, Vol. 149 (July 2, 1965), pp. 22-33. Leakey's own major report of his work is being published in 3 volumes: *Olduvai Gorge 1951-1961*; Volume 1 (1965) is on geology and fauna; Volume 2 will describe the hominid remains found; Volume 3 will discuss the excavated cultures. For a warning on the unreliability of fluorine dating methods for fossil bone analysis, see *Science*, Vol. 136 (April 20, 1962), pp. 241-244. However, most of the Olduvai dates were established by potassium isotope methods; see *National Geographic*, October 1961, p. 590.

the middle Pleistocene period, between a million and a hundred thousand years ago. Only a few skull fragments are certain, but they are consistent with the developmental hypothesis. The skeletal data and the cultural data are more abundant for more recent times.[40] The Neanderthals who roamed Europe and western Asia 40 to 75,000 years ago have left much evidence of their existence and their primitive culture. These skeletons exhibit some similarities as well as significant differences when compared with those of modern man. Most anthropologists do not consider that the detailed description of how the body of *homo sapiens* developed is yet conclusively settled. They agree that it had developed by 20 to 40,000 years ago, this conclusion being based on radiocarbon and geological dating of Cro-Magnon sites in Europe and Asia where many modern-type fossils are found. These data are to be accounted for by whatever means one may choose, but they may not be honestly or consistently ignored, nor passed off as spurious.

Before interpreting these physical data, we must, to be consistent in the Christian view, adduce also the Biblical data that relate to the development and creation of man.

> And God said, let us make man in our image, and after our likeness, and let them have dominion over (the other creatures) . . . Male and female created He them. . . .
>
> And the Lord God formed man of the dust of the ground, and breathed into his nostrils the breath of life; and man became a living soul. . . .

The word "breath" here has the same Hebrew root as the word "spirit." In a later passage, describing the creation of man in more detail, the statement is made that God placed the "man whom He had formed" in a pleasant garden with trees good for food. The geography of that place (Eden) is

---

[40] See, for example, J. D. Clark, "The Later Pleistocene Culture of Africa," *Science*, Vol. 150 (Nov. 12, 1965), p. 833. See also Th. Dobzhansky, *Mankind Evolving* (1962), which points up the interdependence of cultural and biological developments in evolution.

obscure, to say the least, but there is some feeling among interpreters that it is in Asia Minor or northern Iraq.[41] Then the man (Adam *means* "man") found that he was lonely; having been given a human personality somehow replicating God's own, he wanted companionship and love. None of the animals could be a "helpmeet" for him, and so God gave him woman. The statement is that a rib of the man was made into the woman. This couple proceeded to multiply, as they were supposed to, but also to rebel against God's authority. Other Biblical passages reveal to us that Adam's rebellious nature was passed along to all his descendants, and that this includes the whole human species, which has moral sensibilities and responsibility to God. More of that part of the story later.

Undoubtedly there are various ways to interpret all these data together, since the physical data are patently incomplete. We shall suggest one possible interpretation, and urge the reader to study the problem for himself and to form his own conclusions using the Christian world view principles enunciated earlier.

It is consistent with the data to distinguish between the development of the body of *homo sapiens,* and the creation of man. The processes of natural selection and biological evolution, possibly with some direct special divine intervention, could have operated for half a billion years to bring the physical part of man into something like its present form.

At some point in time, perhaps 20,000 years ago, perhaps earlier, one of the primate products of the God-designed biological processes had a body somewhat similar to the human body of today. The brain was convoluted enough, the physiological aspects of intelligence and consciousness were

[41] Does the difficulty in finding the four rivers lie in the possibility that the actual Edenic time was so long ago that major geological changes have occurred in that part of the world since then? As recently as 20,000 years ago the Persian Gulf extended to about where Baghdad is now.

there, and it was time for God to culminate creation. God took this primate, and made a man of him. That is, *He put a spirit and a personality in him which was enough like God's own that he could have fellowship with God.* "God made man in His image." This was a new departure, an act of creation; not the creation of a new physical body, but of a personality. Scientific evidence does not speak on such matters. Science may describe how the body came to be; the revelation of God tells us why man came to be the *person* he is, and only enough descriptive physical detail is given to lay a framework for subsequent historical events. From this time on, man was on the scene, and the animal species from which he came (subhuman spiritually, not physically) perhaps an early paleolithic homonoid type, became extinct through inability to compete.

The interpretation of the story about special creation of Eve is difficult. It could have happened just the way Michelangelo depicted it on the Sistine Chapel ceiling, but it seems unlikely that God would resort to such special *fiat* when His own "natural" laws could operate. The purpose[42] in the story is obvious — man and wife are to consider themselves one flesh. Certainly God created both male and female, and it is reasonable to believe that when the man became lonely, God made a woman out of a female subhuman primate. This one too was then no longer an animal, but a full human, with the personality God gave her, able to be a "helpmeet" and companion. "God caused a deep sleep to fall upon Adam," and this may have been the time of a dream about losing a rib from which Eve came. God has used dreams to teach a truth on many occasions. Adam and his descendants were supposed to learn that married life is a unifying relationship. One little known fact is that the Hebrew word "rib" is not the usual one meaning "anatomical rib," but is a word meaning "curve" or "arch"; this may not be

---

[42] Remember the need to consider the purposes of the recording historian in interpreting the history!

significant, for the sense of the passage indicates "anatomical rib."[43]

There are those Christians who feel they can consistently interpret the whole passage in Genesis as myth, with truth germs or symbols in it. Others feel a compulsion to deal with it word by word. The interpretation here takes account of the earlier given definitions and criteria for literal interpretation, which do not preclude recognizing obviously prescientific and cultural elements of the narratives. The whole passage is a part of God's revelation to man. Since that revelation concerns Himself it (1) is more occupied with relationship to God and morality than with scientific description; (2) is accurate in its prescientific way in whatever description it does give.

(d) Conclusion

The "image of God" is certainly nonphysical, for "God is a spirit, and they that worship Him must do so in spirit and in truth" (John 4:24). *It is this spiritual side of man that characterizes him,* in the Christian view, and *the bodily form is quite incidental.* The abilities to use tools, to paint on their cave walls, even to bury their dead in set patterns (as the Neanderthals did), are not the primary distinguishing features of real man. Thus even though anthropologists may use these abilities as the criterion for man-ness, we must remember that as scientists, they are necessarily dealing only with the physical part of man.

The difference between Adam and his erstwhile primate associates was not physical but spiritual. Adam, whether stooped or with low forehead or hairy chest, had, before

[43] Author's personal note: In keeping with the scientific attitude of tentativeness, I am open to new data as it comes, or to consider new interpretations that equally well serve all the existing data. I do not personally feel that the problem of Eve's origin is unsurmountable, nor important enough to invalidate the rest of the interpretation. However, I do not present this interpretation as a final truth, but only as a way I have worked out to account for the data.

his rebellion, a spiritual nature that could commune directly with the holy, eternal Creator-God. We of Western civilization who are rooted in Greek thought are emotionally attached to the notion that Adam was physically a Greek hero, perfectly proportioned according to our present gymnastic standards. But the scriptures only say Adam was innocent, and that the creation was "good," presumably viewed by God's own norms of goodness and emphatically not by ours.

We reiterate that the facts of science, which are so readily interpreted on the basis of evolution, are as philosophically neutral as any other scientific data. Evolution, even applied to *homo sapiens,* is not a philosophical principle but a means of biological description. Persons of both religious and antireligious views might equally well encompass this scientific principle within their views; evolution is not ammunition for one view against another, nor the exclusive property of the irreligious. As we have seen, the consistent Christian *needs* some such hypothesis to assist him in accounting for the vast amount of physical data he has, which is not explicitly discussed in the Biblical record of revelation. In addition, the Christian has the spiritual data to show him that *he is a created spiritual being with moral responsibility to God,* and that the intended fullness of his human potential is to be realized only when he becomes reconciled to God.

3. *The Origins of Society*

The scientific evidence concerning origins of society includes Neanderthal cave paintings and rock carvings; both old and late Stone Age campsites that contain charred bones and worked flint tools[44]; late Stone Age communities (Jarmo, in Iraq, and sections of Anatolia in southern Turkey) in which evidence exists for some beginnings of wheat-raising and of settling into one place; other Neolithic settlements

[44] J. D. Clark, *op. cit.* See also his bibliography for African references.

over much of Asia Minor and southern Europe, in which houses were built and some early elements of communal society are seen (e.g., Hacilar). As the dates of these primitive societies become more recent there is correspondingly more data, and also an evident progress from small nomadic group existence toward fixed agricultural and political societies. The data also include the cultures of modern-day primitive peoples, central Australian, New Guinean, central African bush people, Amazonian Indians, and others.

The artifacts of the Near-Eastern primitive societies indicate that certainly by 7,000 B.C., and perhaps earlier, some consciousness of God or gods was present among the people. In the naturalistic philosophical view this consciousness developed, arising originally from dreams or other mystifying natural occurrences. However, it is a fact to be explained that in many of the primary cultures, not only polytheism was practiced, but also within the divine hierarchy there was a High God, a suggestion of a Supreme Spirit.[45]

The Fertile Crescent cultures urbanized and societies precipitated rather suddenly around 4,000 B.C.[46] Previously for perhaps 2,500 years small agricultural community existence was the way of life of Mesopotamia. Before that existence was more nomadic, in family groups, with little or no domestication of plants or animals, but with hunting tools and semi-permanent caves or campsites.

How does this scientific evidence fit in with scriptural statements concerning early society? At this point, the reader should peruse chapters 4 to 11 of Genesis, with as few pre-

[45] W. Schmidt, a Catholic, in *Primitive Revelation* (1939), presents and interprets much data that an agnostic such as Frazer, *The Golden Bough* (1958), never mentions. By reading many authors of differing viewpoints, one gets a greater amount of data, and some feeling for how to balance opposing views involved in their interpretation.

[46] See *Scientific American*, September 1960, for a series of articles on the subjects under discussion here. Practice distinguishing fact from interpretation, for there are many statements in each category. See also K. V. Flannery, "The Ecology of Early Food Production in Mesopotamia," *Science*, Vol. 147 (March 12, 1965), pp. 1247-1256.

conceptions as possible on how to interpret this passage. Remember also that before Genesis 12, we are glimpsing "prehistory."

The flavor of these early narratives is clearly that of unurbanized small group living; Cain's "city" in Genesis 4:17 need not carry modern connotations. Some of the descendants of Adam, through two of his sons (Cain and Seth), are mentioned. Similarities in the names of various ones in each of the two family lines need be no more coincidental than names often are in families, especially in the East.[47] Down the history of Cain's family we find men who made significant cultural contributions, in such diverse areas of achievement as agriculture, the arts, and metallurgy.

But it is the *other* family line, that of Seth (whose name means "appointed"), with which the revelation of God is more concerned, for it is from this line that Abraham came, and ultimately the human bodily vehicle for God's personal revelation in Jesus Christ. During Seth's time "man began to call themselves by the name of Jehovah" (Gen. 4:26 marg.), and later references are made to them as "sons of God" as distinct from the "sons of men" (Gen. 6:2).

The line of Seth, which began with Adam's knowledge of God, led downward spiritually until God found it necessary, in His own infinite wisdom and loving purposes, to destroy the apostate. One man, Noah, "found grace in the eyes of the Lord," and Noah had enough faith to obey God,[48] although just how God spoke isn't made clear. The "sons of God" were purified by flood, and God promised never again to destroy as He did, as long as the earth remains. After or during a long time with many intervening generations, some names of which are listed in Genesis 10, the de-

---

[47] Some hold that the various early manuscripts are being copied here without regard for harmonization — that these lists are one list repeated twice and partly garbled. This interpretation is inadmissible in the Christian view.

[48] This is the pattern of God's dealings with men; His grace acts, our faith accepts in obedience (Eph. 2:8-10).

scendants of Noah began to urbanize, and to form into a political unit. It was an abortive attempt, because of their impiety in approaching God through other means than those originally specifically revealed, known to Noah and others. They attempted a ziggurat worship instead of the sacrificial recognition of their personal sins.[49] Apparently they couldn't get along with each other in the unification attempt, due to confusion of languages.[50] God's purposes were not to be thwarted by mere human political or linguistic amalgamation, and He worked (possibly through "natural" laws of behavior) to break up the deviant from truth lest it further corrupt the already dimming consciousness of the one true God.

At the end of a long line of descendants from Noah's son, Shem, we find the next major stopping place in the historical narrative, the man Abram. It is not relevant to discuss, or even to mention, all the intervening generations from Noah to Abraham; some are given in Genesis 11:10-32, in varying detail. When a name is given, the age of that person or his dynasty is normally given, but in view of Oriental genealogical practice, it is safe to assume that only outstanding per-

[49] E.g., Abel (Gen. 4:1-4), Noah (Gen. 8:20).
[50] In Genesis 10:5, 20, and 31, there are statements concerning the differing languages of the descendants of Noah's sons. Genesis 11:1, which indicates that Noah's whole family had one basic language, would therefore refer back to a prehistoric time soon after the flood. The tower of Babel incident, Genesis 11:1, possibly expands these statements of Genesis 10. Another possibility is that some of the later descendants of Noah, who by this time had begun to acquire differing dialects or languages, attempted to unify the family. They set out to build themselves a central place of approach to God, ignoring God's revealed will concerning worship. As part of their unification attempt, a single ancient language was to be adopted and preserved. Yet another possibility for interpreting this passage is that it describes the origins of Mesopotamian tower worship, as developed by the ancestors of Abraham. As we proceed through Genesis 4-11, the scope narrows from all mankind (Adam) to a specific family line (Seth) to another specific line of descent (Noah). Here it narrows further, to those who settled in Mesopotamia, and summarizes an event that may have taken a long time, the building of a large tower and the development of different languages among the generations of builders.

sonages in the line are mentioned. (Ussher's chronology which simply adds stated ages was long an embarrassment, for if it is applied to pre-Abrahamic times it leads to dates which are much too late to be realistic. This chronological interpretation is unnecessary, of course.)

The whole Biblical narrative is characterized by its skipping over irrelevant historical items and dwelling at length on some personality or event, before skipping on to another, with or without a warning phrase. While this type of narrative is sometimes hard for us to fit in with other historical data, it suits God's purposes in revelation, for He wants us to learn certain lessons about Himself, and scientific inquiry for its own sake is secondary to that purpose.

In interpreting the passage Genesis 6-9 itself, we need not think of the flood as universal or world-wide in terms of our present knowledge of the earth. It was "world-wide" in terms of that culture's geographical understanding. It is an illustration of the judgment of God in the last days, and is so alluded to in the New Testament by Christ Himself as well as others (Matt. 24:36-44). But no world-wide geological or geographical evidence exists for a flood of the proportions described.[51] Atavistic legends of such an event have been found widespread over the globe in many primitive cultures. A consistent interpretation of these facts is that the flood was a judgment upon the decadent line of Seth, the line of Cain having already widely dispersed, being not the line through which God was revealing Himself.

In support of this interpretation is the assertion in Genesis that Cain's descendant, Tubal-Cain, was a metal worker. Now the late Stone Age and early Bronze Age overlap to some extent, but copper or bronze was not found in the "Fertile Crescent" village archaeology before about 4,000 B.C. Until that time the people, for all their agricultural development, were still neolithic. But long before this time, men

[51] See B. Ramm, op. cit., pp. 229ff., for a discussion of "Flood Geology."

(not merely the *homo sapiens* body, but humans with spiritual consciousness) were globally dispersed, in the Americas, in Africa, in Australia, in Europe. A way to fit these data together is to think of the lines of Cain and Seth as distinct, both lines beginning at the time of Adam, perhaps as early as 20,000 B.C. (See Figure 3 for a pictorial demonstration of this thesis.) Cain's line led ultimately through the earliest copper workers, who possibly found hard chunks of this queer, reddish, shiny, hard stuff in campfires built on green rocks. This discovery was put to use in Asia Minor around 4,000 B.C. In the meanwhile, earlier members of Cain's line had dispersed themselves pretty well over the globe, with their somewhat diluted knowledge of the one High God, but with an ever accumulating host of other lesser deities whose placation seemed more immediate.

The distinct line of Seth started to grow in numbers as well, but without geographic dispersal, and it developed more directly under the tutelage of Adam, the man who had personally known God in the way all men were intended to know God. Although Adam had rebelled and had been driven out from the place of fellowship, he had taught Seth, and Seth taught his children, and so on, something of the means of knowing and approaching God. Of such a privileged people God expected a response of obedient faith; instead, the basically egocentric human heart gradually rejected the knowledge of God. In Romans 1:20-32 we find a picture of this dismal process in its true perspective. With Noah, God started afresh His purposes of revealing Himself to mankind. In this view, Noah also was a neolithic man, living in the same general region with others of the "sons of God," i.e., descendants of Seth, possibly a valley in the Fertile Crescent hills from which they later descended to the plains of Mesopotamia. Noah saved his immediate family from the destruction which came upon the rest of his neighbors, and continued the line of Seth. The date of the Deluge of Genesis 6-9 must have been also very early, so that descendants of

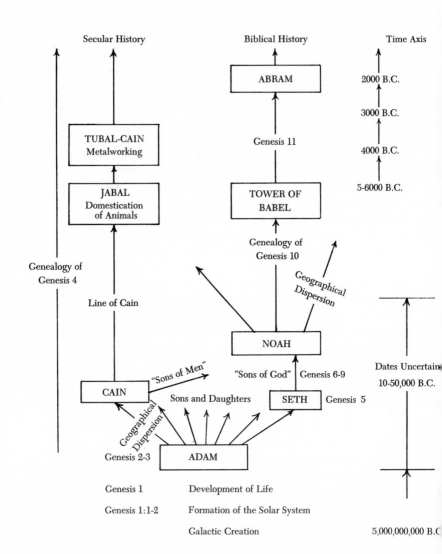

FIGURE 3. A Diagram to Illustrate an Interpretation of the Early Chapters of Genesis in Terms of Known Chronology

Noah through Japheth and Ham who spread throughout the world before about 10,000 B.C. carried this flood story with them, and it became a part of the legends of many (but not all) ethnic groups. Sometime in the course of the history of Noah's descendants the attempt to form a single political and religious state was made, and the resulting confusion caused dispersion of still more of these descendants.

Through Noah's son Shem, after many generations, came Abram, or Abraham, about 2,000 B.C. Meanwhile, people of both Cain's and Seth's lines had begun to domesticate animals (Jabal gets the credit in Genesis 4:20) and to cultivate plants such as wheat. They began to live together in villages and farm with wooden and stone tools, around 10,000 to 7,000 B.C. Pottery was invented around 5,000 B.C. in this area. Still later, larger cities began to be founded — the incident of language confusion at Babel's ziggurat may fit at this point in the chronology — societies such as the Sumerian, Akkadian (early Assyrian), and Egyptian came into being. Bronze (copper) began to be worked at about this time, and may have given one of these political entities some temporary advantage, but the use of copper soon became widespread. The reader is referred to encyclopedia articles on archaeology, Assyria, Babylon, and Egypt, to pick up the story from about 3,000 B.C. on. Religiously conscious men began to ally themselves into societies and civilizations, and to write about themselves at this time.

The interpretation here placed on the necessarily incomplete physical data from anthropology and archaeology, and on that revealed in early Genesis, is admittedly tentative. It does seem to account for the data consistently, and is presented only as an illustration of how a Christian can (and should try to) interpret all available data in the context of his world view. The reader is not urged necessarily to agree with the interpretations given, but rather to attempt his own consistent interpretations of the available raw data.

C. Aberrations

One other widely observable data category that some use against the Christian view is the existence of un-Christlike practices among Christian people. It is alleged that, since professing Christians apparently behave and misbehave just as non-Christians do, there is no substance to Christ's claim to be able to overcome egocentricity in the life of the believer.

In the Christian view, such behavior is interpreted as aberrations from the revealed norm.[52] It is convenient to analyze these practices in terms of shifts of emphasis from the ideal, i.e., scriptural, patterns. Every person has his own personality, with its own balance of constituent elements. We are all compounded of emotion, volition, and intellect; we all have the basic needs and drives that, taken together, comprise human nature. Individuality results from the slightly different ways each of us goes about to meet these needs, to integrate a personality out of these sundry elements. Normalcy is the broad category into which most of us fit by virtue of our ways of resolving inner conflicts as we face and fulfill these basic drives. Identical personalities rarely if ever develop, but the range of variation for normalcy is defined to be great enough to accommodate most people. As George Orwell put it in *1984*, sanity is statistical. Thus among us in free society we find personalities developed with more or less emphasis on each of the composite aspects: emotion, volition, or intellect. Only when an emphasis is extreme, or behavior becomes bizarre, do we generally consider a person to be unbalanced.

Each personality type, and each individual within each type, tends to have his own variety of religious experience. The emphasis placed on emotion, on will (decision or

---

[52] See C. S. Lewis, *Mere Christianity* (1960), Chap. 10, in "Beyond Personality," "Nice People or New Men," for a typically clear Lewisian analysis.

morality), or on intellectual aspects of faith thus varies widely within the bounds of Christendom. Much of this variation is necessary and a normal part of God's design, as are the different personality types. There is an allowable (normal) range of variability for the ways people's personalities may balance between these three emphases. The particular balance point is dynamic, resulting in the case of a Christian from the person's own individual relationship with Jesus Christ. The balance point shifts as the growing personality changes, deepens, or broadens. The balance between these three diverse psychical elements, for all people, is a complex function of one's genetic and environmental make-up; the latter apparently depends in turn on childhood, familial, and other interpersonal relationships and experiences.

1. *Emotionalism*

Since human personality contains emotional factors, it is to be expected that God would deal with us in at least partly emotional ways. He *is* love; He loves us, and wants us to respond with our love, a basic emotional appeal. He shows us our rebellion against His love, and thereby evokes our shame, another emotional appeal, and also one that issues in action, i.e., repentance.[53] He shows us the alternatives, eternal joy in His presence, or the torment of eternal banishment from His glory; again eliciting basic emotions, hope or fear. He illumines His children spiritually to see the real needs of their fellow worldlings and arouses compassion, yet another emotion which leads to action. There is nothing wrong *per se* with the appeal to emotion.

There is something wrong, however, when a Christian, or anybody else for that matter, lets his emotions have control in his personality. A mature, integrated person has feelings, and they are in balance with his will, conscience, and rationality. The will is in control, acting upon both feel-

53 II Corinthians 7:10.

ings and knowledge within bounds prescribed by conscience. For a Christian this means ideally that his will is made aware of God's will through objective study of the Bible and through subjective promptings of God's Spirit. Action directed by the will is zeal with knowledge, since the God-given (and spiritually awakened) intellect is feeding information to the will, with the emotions primarily supplying the drive for obedience.

The criterion for propriety of emotionalism in Christianity is the emphasis placed on it relative to that put on the other personality facets, as compared with the Biblical emphasis. As noted, there is a broad range of proper emphasis because people, their needs, and their ways of response are all different. But if a pulpit appeal or a point of view explicitly or implicitly denies a place to intellect or will, then there is lack of balance. The place of intellect is to process data, to reason upon the basis of the assumed faith, as was discussed earlier. The place of the will is to decide, to choose an interpretation or action befitting the data at hand, and conforming to standards of conscience. Emotion provides the drive to accomplish the action.

When a person hears of his personal need of God's forgiveness and of the proffered salvation in Christ, there is bound to be an emotional response. If this is the only response, it is insufficient; and tearfully going forward at the close of a meeting, signing a decision card, lighting a candle, or any other formality means nothing unless the emotional response leads to rational appraisal of the gospel and willful acceptance of Christ as Lord and Savior.[54] A person whose emotions only are exercised often hardens his real decision-making capability against acceptance when the emotional jag wears off. The propriety of using emotional evangelistic appeals depends on the *way these appeals are made*. If the good news of forgiveness of sin, of salvation

[54] Cf. Parable of the Sower (Mark 4).

by grace through faith, is presented *in such a way that the whole human personality can interact with the message,* then the proper balance is apt to be present between the emotional, intellectual, and volitional elements. An unbalanced presentation of Christ to the world is a misrepresentation, nullifying the profession that the Lord can make men whole.

It is deplorable that some ostensibly Christian individuals and groups may repel the more intellectual personality types seeking truth. It is also deplorable that these seeking ones may not be mature enough to understand that one tree does not make the forest, that unbalance is a deviation from the way of real Christianity. A seeker after truth in Christ ought to understand that Jesus can meet his own individual need. The misplaced emphases are explicable within the Christian world view as representing improper comprehension of the fullness, breadth, and depth of Christ's interaction with the full range of our own human personalities.

2. *Intellectualism*

Just as overemphasis of emotion in our Christian experience is to be avoided, so is a cold, proud intellectualism. Since this emphasis leads to less overt and bizarre effects than emotional unbalance, society places less disapproval on religious intellectualism than on emotionalism. However, in the Christian view any unbalance is wrong, and detours us from the perfect way God desires for us individually.

Intellectualism, in the sense of an excess, has many forms, all characterized by some failure to recognize the inherent limitations of the human intellect. It is possible for Christians to take their rationality too seriously, even being aware that they must depend ultimately upon God for wisdom. It is easy for one to fall into the temptation to "think of himself more highly than he ought to think," to be proud of intellectual abilities, or to use them in status-seeking, though he knows better, and while he pays lip service to the principles of I Corinthians 1:18-30.

Among these perverted forms of intellectualism is what might be called "scientism," an abdication of the Christian's responsibility and right to piece together a world view for himself which is Christian as well as consistent with scientific observations. There are those who, in their desperate efforts never to be wrong or out-of-date, accept at face value anything a Ph.D. scientist declares.[55] The currents of scientific thought are variable enough to embarrass one who is so unstable as to place scientific *interpretation* on a par with scriptural *statements*. (Remember the distinction to be made between raw data and interpretations in both science and Christianity.) Remember also that scientific data are incomplete. Yet whole segments of nominal Christendom have abandoned their reason, ironically in the name of reason, and practice scientism, complete with its antisupernatural overtones.

Another form of intellectualism is dead orthodoxy. Here we find correct creeds, even well-thought-out theological expositions. But the life is missing, because the intellect is overemphasized, to the exclusion of the human need for some emotional response to God. Impregnable theological and apologetic systems are erected, but no one wants to live within these fortifications because there is no fire by which to warm the soul.

A seeker after truth wants something that makes sense, but he wants also something that gives meaning to life, that can be vital to him. Christ was a warm person toward sincere seekers, as well as personifying "the wisdom of God." Paul was an intellectual in every sense of the word, but was also a vital person with strong emotional drives. When one sees cold intellectualism along with frequently concomitant hypocrisy and snobbery in a church group, even though the doctrine be unassailably orthodox, he may well be repelled

[55] I hope there are none such among my readers; my intention is to stimulate some analytic and critical thinking instead of blind acceptance (or rejection!) of my ideas.

because he encounters nothing there that brings him into that vital relationship with God which, deep inside, he subjectively knows that he needs.

3. Legalism

Overemphasis of one or another of the elements in a Christian personality leads to deviation from the pattern God desires for that person. Undue emphasis on the volitional aspect sets up a tendency toward self-righteousness; that is, an inordinately strong-willed person is apt to take pride in his own ability to keep the moral code he imagines God has set. Saint Paul remarked that he had suffered the loss of all things, including any claims he might have had to ceremonial righteousness by virtue of his birth or his own actions in keeping Jewish law. He states that he counted all things loss relative to the knowledge of Christ, so that he might "be found in Him, not having mine own righteousness which is of the law," but that which is in Christ.[56] Thus the basic character of self-righteousness is its professed adherence to some moral code, a "law." The person who keeps some law as his means of recommending himself to God, or of earning his salvation, is practicing self-righteousness. The law may be the Ten Commandments, or another Biblically-based code of ethics; it may be the conventions of some groups, or it may be individually devised. The principle is the same: the person who tries to keep any rules in order to gain religious merit thereby for himself, is implicitly claiming that he is able by his own will to achieve God's standard of righteousness.

The logical futility of such a claim should be clear, for our motives are an integral part of our actions as seen by the God who looks into hearts rather than upon external appearances. If motives are self-willed, as they are when one attempts to acquire some religious merit by his own efforts,

[56] Philippians 3:7-10.

these motives corrupt even an otherwise good or neutral act and render it selfish. It is therefore impossible to earn acceptance with God. This form of legalism, the self-righteous effort to keep a law of some sort as a means of salvation, must thus be considered as an aberration from true Christianity.

Nearly every Christian denomination or group, from Roman Catholic to Darbyite-Exclusive Brethren, has its own conventional *mores* and taboos, codified or not. Many of these rules are scripturally based, to be sure. But many are neither scriptural nor contrary to the revelation; they are simply conventions, traditional within the particular group. Such behavior patterns are partly a natural consequence of the different interpretational emphases different people place on the scripture, and they need not be wrong in themselves. As with the other Christian aberrations resulting from the lack of balance, there is a range of normalcy, for God deals with different individuals in different ways, and with the same individual differently at various stages of his Christian experience and development.[57]

However, when a Christian group emphasizes its law-keeping to the practical neglect of God's ways of dealing in grace, then that group, or individuals in it, are deviating from the "simplicity that is in Christ." When a Christian forgets that he is saved by God's mercy, and lets the concept creep into his mind that he can gain some extra favor, or can bargain with God, by *doing something* — keeping some rules of his group, or his own, even scripturally-based rules — he is "falling from grace." He is losing some of the fullness of the knowledge of God that is intended for him. Legalistic thinking tends to make us narrow-minded, dogmatic, and un-Christlike. For example, the legalistic Puritan notion of worldliness which would limit the enjoyment of life as sinful *per se* is decidedly un-Biblical.

[57] See, for example, I Corinthians 8, and Romans 14, for the principles involved.

This is not to condone antiscriptural practice, nor disobedience to God's revealed principles or laws, which is sin. Rather, we must be careful of our reasons for our actions, and our attitudes in them, lest we act from such motives as status-seeking in our own group, or bargaining for God's favor. These motives and attitudes are sinful, too.

The tendency is strong in us to set up codes of action for ourselves. We are given few actual Biblical rules, but rather many principles that can be applied in diverse situations in life. To apply these principles requires dependence upon God Himself to guide us daily by His Spirit — "we walk by faith." It is really easier, that is, less rigorous intellectually or volitionally, for us to have a set of inflexible rules to obey, that require little or no thought of how they are to be applied in various life-situations. Like little children, we gain some sense of security from being circumscribed by tangible regulations, and we don't seem to want to mature spiritually to the point of being guided by the less tangible principles of behavior.

Paul's inspired remarks to the Colossians bear on this point.

> So, if, through your faith in Christ, you are dead to the principles of this world, why, as if you were still part of this world-wide system, do you take the slightest notion of these purely human prohibitions — 'don't touch this,' 'don't taste that,' and 'don't handle the other'? 'This,' 'that,' and 'the other' will all pass away after use. I know that these regulations look wise with their self-inspired efforts at worship, their policy of self-humbling and their studied neglect of the body. But in actual practice they do honour, not to God, but to man's own pride (Col. 2:20-23, Phillips).

Paul again, writing under inspiration to the church at Galatia, focusses on the problem of legalism:

> Christ has made us completely free; stand fast then and do not again be hampered with the yoke of slavery [to the law] . . . You have lost the good of union with Christ if you seek acquittal by Law: You have fallen from grace. For in spirit and owing to our faith we wait in hope of our acceptance.

> In Christ Jesus neither circumcision nor uncircumcision [formal legalism] is of any avail; but only faith working through love. . . .
>
> You indeed, brethren were called to freedom. Only do not make your freedom an incentive to your lower nature; but serve one another in love . . . (Gal. 5:1, 4, 5, 13, Weymouth).

The Galatians apparently were being swayed by those who wanted them to submit formally to becoming Jews before they could become, or remain, Christians. The principle to notice in this passage is that God calls us into liberty, freedom in actions, and not to rigidity or narrowness of a legal code. "Where the Spirit of the Lord is, there is liberty." A person who loves God as he should can do anything he wants, can ask for and receive anything he wants, because such a one is free to seek what God wants for him, and free to do God's will. He is not bound by a code of his own, or other human, devising; he is bound by the bands of love, and that is perfect freedom, although not license.

Legalistic thinking among the various branches of Protestantism is the most widespread and subtle of the observable deviations from basic Christianity. Among the theologically "liberal," legalism is thinly disguised as social action; their whole concept of God's holiness, of sin, and of salvation is based on too high an appraisal of the human ability to know God by reason and moral activity. Among the fundamentalists the principles of God's grace are generally paid some lip service; the scriptural teaching is recognized that a man cannot save himself but must accept God's free gift. However, legalistic concepts arise among those who claim the grace of God, for reasons just mentioned, and these concepts often lead to attitudes and practices that confuse the issues of salvation for a truth-seeker.[58] Regardless of what he is told — "come to Jesus just as you are, He can save you" — the sincere seeker after the truth-he-knows-not-yet is often con-

[58] Joseph Bayly, *The Gospel Blimp* (1960).

fused by the sermon emphasis on not smoking, not dancing, not drinking, not doing this, or that, or the other. Is one's approach to God through Christ contingent upon his acceptance of these conventional ethical standards?

If salvation is by God's grace then it is not by any of our works; on the other hand, if it could be by means of any work of our own, any legal action, then it cannot be of God's grace. Otherwise the words "works" and "grace" have lost their meanings (Rom. 11:5-6). A non-Christian who has studied the Bible enough to know the meanings of these words will certainly find much foolishness being preached, in both fundamental and liberal churches, where it is often implied that a person needs to do, or not do, something, in order to merit God's grace. This is not the "foolishness of the cross"; it is the inconsistency of the human heart, the subtle legalism so common in modern church groups. Christians need to sound the trumpet clearly, to "preach the gospel of the *grace* of God," so that hearers will see themselves as able to do nothing except to cast themselves upon that unmeritable favor for salvation by faith.

4. *Balance, or Normalcy*

A word about normalcy in the Christian life is in order after the remarks about aberrations. One should not conclude from the earlier discussions that the Christian life is a bed of roses, at least not thornless roses. The normal Christian life is in dynamic balance, and it is to be lived in dependence upon God to work out within us His purposes for us individually and collectively. "The fruit of the Spirit is love, joy, peace . . . ," all personality traits. Yet these traits and attitudes result from conflicts that are always going on within us. It is said that God deals with us as sons, chastening as necessary to remove rebellious streaks, and that the "peaceable fruit of righteousness" is for those "who are exercised" by such dealings. It is said that the flesh and the spirit are at war within us. This is not the conflict of a neurotic personality at war with itself over repressed data; rather it is the action of God within the redeemed human personality developing the potential of that personality for being whole. Ernest White explores this conflict between spiritual forces within the believer, and his remarks are recommended reading.[59] The Christian, realizing objectively the dynamic nature of his new spiritual life in Christ, may have the full assurance of faith that the "battle is the Lord's," and have the concomitant deeply seated joy and peace of that vicarious victory. There is no excuse in this for laziness, intellectual or otherwise, nor for relaxed vigilance against the sinful attitudes or actions that so easily beset us. But neither is there any reason for extensive despairing introspection that discourages the soul because of a legalistic approach to our actions. Remember the words of the Lord Jesus:

> These things have I spoken unto you, that in Me ye might have peace. In the world ye shall have tribulation: but be of good cheer; I have overcome the world (John 16:33).

The standard for Christian normalcy is the New Testament teaching of Jesus and the apostles; for example, such passages as John 14-16, Romans 6-8, and 12-14, I Corinthians 11-14, Ephesians 4-6. The revealed basis of the Christian life is that God Himself lives spiritually in the true believer. The daily life is to be lived in dependence upon God to do in us what He has revealed He will do if we but let Him. The difficulty in discipleship lies in "letting Him," in acquiescence. The hardest thing for one to do is to yield one's self, his self-achievement principle, or his innate (and sinful or egocentric) tendency to think he can please God by himself. The practical "holiness without which no man shall see God" is the result of God's own working in us. This divine enabling is given in response to our recognition of our personal inability, coupled with our dependence upon Him to do in us what He has promised. "This is the victory that overcomes the world,

[59] *Op. cit.*, Chapter XI, p. 97.

even our faith." What He has promised is (among other things) to guide us in all decisions, to change our minds and attitudes so that we desire to do good rather than evil, and to strengthen our faith in proportion to our need in the face of worldly trials He allows to come our way. These promises of God are rarely claimed fully, which is another way of saying that no one of us in the flesh fully trusts God, fully loves Him, or fully follows His revealed will. Growth in the Christian life takes place in the direction of more dependence upon God to work out His will in our personal lives. This developing faith is normal Christian experience. Such a person, growing in grace, has no room for pride, nor a persecution complex, nor for the personality aberrations already described. A person who becomes preoccupied with his own spiritual status or abilities begins to lose the real power of God in his life, for that power stems solely from preoccupation with the knowledge of God.

The underlying motivation and purpose in all that a Christian person does should be his love for God. We are told that we are not our own, but we are bought with a price, and that therefore we are to glorify God in our bodies and in our spirits, which are God's. We are told to set our affection on things above where Christ is glorified with God. Faith recognizes these truths and responds by love for God, as we have discussed earlier. The basic motive in life serves to organize the personality so that every decision, every attitude, every action, in every facet of daily living, can be made consciously or unconsciously subservient to the principles revealed as God's will in scripture. No human perfectly lives up to this standard of living to please God, and our specific failures in action and attitude are directly traceable to some reversion toward egocentricity away from love for God. However, God Himself lives in the believer and, reminding us of our shortcomings, He leads us to confession, receipt of His forgiveness, and a closer fellowship with Himself. Within this fellowship, God will provide all the spiritual resources we need to make us what His loving design has called out for our lives. This walk with God, as a small child with his father, is normal Christian experience.

D. CONCLUSIONS

In this chapter we have briefly discussed three broad problem areas in order to show how a Christian can approach the data available to him. Both the raw data of science — observations — and those of revelation — Biblical statements and subjective experience — have been taken as grist for the interpretative mill of the Christian world view. Many more data exist relating to these and to other fields of interest. Some of this information is referenced in footnotes and bibliography, some is yet to be discovered. The suggestions for interpreting the data presented are given tentatively, with the claim only that they account for the data consistently. No claim is made that these interpretations of the data are the correct, unique, or final ones; a correct view must, however, account for the same raw data as well as any new data that comes along. This attitude illustrates our Christian world view principles: (1) of the philosophical neutrality of data, and the need for a view or theory to guide the assignment of meaning to data, and (2) of the need for intellectual honesty in assessing and accounting for all available data.

1. *The Bible*

The rather uniform testimony of the Middle Eastern archaeologist is that archaeology (1) supports the general features and many of the specific details of the Biblical historical narratives; and (2) conversely, does not directly contradict those narratives, although it is often silent (remember the incompleteness of physical data). In making this statement, we are using the Christian world view principle that it is the raw data from our data categories that agree, and not necessarily data already processed by some theory or view. Also, we remember that the disparity in essence between physical and spiritual realities — the "otherness" of the spiritual — implies that even if every historical statement of the Bible text were to be unequivocally proved true by scientific methods, we would still have no proof that the Bible is an inspired record of God's revelation to us. This is still, and always must be, a matter of faith for the Christian. The historicity of the Bible is consistent with our assumption that the Bible records God's revelation. Since proof *is* consistency, this is as "proved" as any world view can claim to be.

There are further consequences of the "otherness" of the spiritual realities that are partly revealed in the objective data of Biblical statements. Since it is the infinite, spiritual, God who (we assume) is revealing Himself in finite, physical terms, we are faced with the problem of interpreting these statements, symbols, and historical events according to principles that are not necessarily the same as we normally use in interpreting physical data. God's stated purpose in revelation is that we humans might know Him whom to know is life eternal and abundant.[60] While the physical details of revelation may be made rationally consistent to our minds, it is crucial that the interpretation of the data involves us more deeply than in mere intellectual ways. To him who is willing to act on God's will, God Himself promises spiritual illumination, and help in interpreting the revealed data. By this means God, through Jesus Christ, reveals Himself to us in every age in ways that are significant and necessary for our lives in that age. The data themselves — inspired statements concerning Christ — do not change from age to age because God does not change. Nor do we humans change except in our understanding and use of the physical universe; our basic human needs for spiritual understanding and fulfillment remain although they may find different expressions at

[60] John 10:10 and 17:3.

different times. The physical symbols (data) of the spiritual realities may thus need to be reinterpreted within an updated rationally consistent world view differing from that held by the ancients or medieval believers, but the Christian view assumes and accepts the eternal spiritual realities represented and revealed. By personal involvement we allow God to harmonize us with these realities. Only by personal involvement do we find fully meaningful interpretations of both the physical and spiritual data.

2. *Origins*

In the discussions of origins of the universe, of life, of man, and of societies of men, we have again illustrated the potential of our Christian world view to handle data. One guiding principle is that science describes observable reality and that meaning is provided by assumptions that are extrascientific — religious or philosophical. The scientific method operates with astronomical, geological, biological, and other physical data, and with the logic of mathematics. There result descriptions of the universe, the galaxy, the earth, and plants and animals, and of man's body, including tentative descriptions as to how these things developed to their present forms. By invoking the Christian assumptions, we find that these entities were all created by God and follow the natural laws He has established. These laws are the ones scientific methods discover and describe. They include the statistical laws of interaction between elementary particles, nuclei, atoms and molecules that underlie all known physical phenomena (perhaps even gravity). The Christian view allows for science to tell us how these material things develop and behave, and then it reveals that God causes all of them to be. He reveals that man is not an accident in the universe, but (as most of us suspected all along and secretly hoped for, too) man has a place and purpose in God's grand temporal and eternal design. It is not very important how God worked to bring man's physical part into being — science says the statistical laws of chemistry, ecology, and sociology were involved. What is important is the eternal, spiritual part of man that inter- acts and can fellowship with God. The few Biblical data that are given concerning physical matters are interpretable in terms of the current understanding given us by science.

(However, in this case, as ever, we must be careful to watch for the principle that it is raw data from science and the Bible that can be harmonized; too many scientists have at- tempted to extrapolate from science into philosophy, and they may cite data that is already processed by world views inimi- cal to the Christian view. This processed data may well be impossible to reconcile with the Bible. Contrariwise, the Christian person may have frozen the interpretation of a Biblical statement, made in the context of an inconsistent world view; this processed data may well be impossible to reconcile with the data of science.)

The interpretations of the data on origins given in this chapter attempt to follow the world view principles. We have reinterpreted data from both categories; we recognize that scientific data are incomplete, and that human under- standing is finite. Therefore the interpretation is tentative as to detail. In general, though, we find that many of the current scientific descriptions are acceptable *as descriptions* of the means God used to bring the world to its present state, and man to his. The data of anthropology are too sparse to provide unequivocal scientific descriptions of the origins of the religious nature of man; the data of the Bible are consis- tent on this point, i.e., they can be interpreted jointly with the raw data we have on primitive cultures: God created man with a spiritual nature. Although the *body* may have done so, the *spiritual nature* of man did not evolve.

3. *Ethical Aberrations*

The third problem area discussed may well be the most critical. The un-Christlike behavior of professing Christians is undoubtedly a larger stumbling block to faith than the possibility of discrepancy between science and the Bible. That is, moral inconsistency looms larger than intellectual inconsistency. It is certainly an observable matter and, as such, needs interpretation. Our Christian world view sees such inconsistent behavior as aberrant from the true norm exemplified for us in the life of Jesus Christ and revealed by the teachings of God's Spirit in the Bible. Our lives are in dynamic balance, and when we overemphasize the emotional, volitional, or intellectual aspects, we err. The norm is a life lived in love for God, where God Himself empowers us. The Christian way *is* intellectually consistent but it is also, and more importantly, morally consistent. It provides a significant ethic and means of satisfying the need to live by that ethic.

VI: *Postlude*

A. Concluding Remarks

The Christian world view outlined has been applied here principally to philosophical problems of validity, rational acceptability, and psychological and moral adequacy. The conclusion is that all the available physical data can be consistently interpreted together within a Biblical Christian philosophical framework. As with any world view, the basic assumptions are to be believed and are not provable except insofar as they allow internal and external consistency. In addition to intellectual consistency, the Christian world view of this book provides both the ends and the means for moral integration of personality, by turning the believer away from egocentricity and toward the love of God. Guilt is thereby resolvable and fulfillment of human personality is achievable within the Christian world view framework. It remains for the believer to avail himself of this potential by full involvement of intellectual, emotional, and volitional aspects of his person with the revealed purposes of God.

An area of application that we have left untouched, but to which the Christian view is especially relevant, is social action. The Biblical Christian view of this book implies approaches to all social problems. Although these problems normally have

175

common roots in egocentric human nature, they also have a special relation to contemporary culture. There are Christian views on sex and marriage, race relations, delinquency, care for the aged, patriotism and war, and other pressing social problems, and the reader is urged to find "the mind of Christ" on these matters in order that he may relate his faith to these parts of his culture in an effective way. We emphasize that it is our *total* world view that is to be so applied to these cultural problems, and this implies that technology and reason have a duty to perform in public affairs. Science can and should be applied in the solutions of the world's problems. However, the application of technology itself is inadequate, incomplete, and foredoomed, unless proper account is taken of the spiritual realities and truths that underlie and relate to these problems.

B. ADVICE TO THE READER

One further bit of advice for the reader: Keep reading! We have only partially explored a few promontories in a vast coastline of available physical and Biblical data. The interpretations we have suggested are considered tentative, as all human interpretation must be if it is honest, but we feel we have fitted the data consistently. Each person, and particularly each specialist in any field of study, must apply these principles of interpretation in his own field and perform his own correlations. We have attempted only to illustrate these principles in order to help an interested student to relate the physical universe describable by science and the spiritual world revealed by Jesus Christ.

The best exercise, aside from careful perusal of the Bible itself, is to apply the critical eye to everything one reads. As suggested earlier, practice the separation of fact from interpretation thereof in all situations. We who seek to know truth should always recognize that some assumed point of view underlies everything we read. This consciousness will go a long way to protect us from being swayed by a point of view unless we want to be. It will give us time to collect enough facts from all of reality to begin to sort them into meaningful patterns, and to apply the Christian world view assumptions in a fully consistent reinterpretation of the data.

One who has learned to make the distinction between the raw and processed data presented should thus read avidly and widely. It is edifying to find diverse bits of information that tie together in the Christian world view; it is especially gratifying to pick up these tidbits from authors who use them as ammunition against a religious or Christian view. It is like throwing a fused grenade back into enemy lines. The Christian has the duty and privilege to relate truth, wherever he finds it, to his knowledge of God. Much truth is to be found in the writings of scholars who are inimical to our view.

Mined ore which contains some desired precious metal atoms must be processed chemically to separate the metal from the residue. Sometimes the metal atoms are tightly bound and hard to extricate. Similarly, some underlying new data are, as reported, tightly bound into atheistic world views, but if extricated they may shine brightly in their place in the Christian view. The point is that we orthodox Christians have everything to gain by aggressively pursuing truths from all sources in both spheres of reality.

There is nothing wrong with having, expressing, or listening to any point of view. Indeed, having a philosophical framework is one mark of maturity, and a means of personality balance; expressing it stems from the human need to be fully involved in our viewpoint; listening to many points of view is a means of education. A wise youth does not marry for mere affection the first girl (or boy) friend; he (or she) gets to know many potential spouses before settling on one. Similarly, the ubiquitous antipathy toward Biblical Christianity notwithstanding, we recommend that an intelligent appraisal be made of this position, which is characterized by faithful reason and by its potentially total consistency. This book was intended to be helpful in making this appraisal — for the sincerely skeptical student as well as for one more sympathetic to Christianity.

To the Christian, our advice is to avoid becoming pre-occupied with philosophical debate or continued questioning of the rational validity of faith. Our minds should be open to new data and new interpretations, but the Christian life does not consist of apologetics, nor is it purely intellectual. Rather, it is a dynamic relationship to Christ that issues in inner peace and joy, in daily decisions to practice the Lord-ship of Christ, and in calm and stable assurance of one's rational consistency. We therefore need not be defensive about our faith, nor always reacting to new attacks from naturalism, humanism, or other views inimical to Christianity. The intellectual conviction that one's faith is reasonable, if ineffable, is a necessary aspect of the Christian life, but it is only a part of the whole. We are to press on toward the high calling we have in Christ, not turning back to exhume dead issues, nor to expend our energies on questions not personally relevant.

C. Summary

Here we will succinctly state the contents of the world view presented, by way of review:

(1) Science, that is, the scientific method, describes the physical universe, by means of (a) data observation, (b) generalization into explanations that account for data, and (c) further experimental verifications of the consistency of the descriptions. The practice of science depends on the three corresponding presuppositions: (a) that there is such a thing as observable physical reality, (b) that this reality is such that its description is logical or self-consistent, and (c) that this reality is causal. (However, the applicable causality need not be deterministic, but in fact appears to be statistical.) Observable data have meaning only within the context of some theory, explanation, or description; the same data may

be explained consistently, although tentatively, by more than one theory at any time. Ultimately, more data will decide between theories, but proof means only that the explanation accounts consistently (without contradiction) for all known data. It is the function of science to provide descriptions that account for presently known observable data. The scientific method does not treat realities that are nonphysical or not observable, and it does not treat questions of ultimate meanings or purposes. In other words, physical data are philosophically neutral.

(2) Meaning and purpose are metascientific, or ascientific concepts. They are the proper domain of philosophy and/or religion rather than of science. In addition to the presuppositions (given above), which allow science to provide consistent descriptions of observable reality, we must make extrascientific presuppositions that lead us to the possible meanings behind the descriptions. These are philosophical presuppositions, and they are necessary for us because the human personality needs to comprehend some meaning, or have some world view. Every person posits these philosophical assumptions, tacitly or knowingly, and uses them to make sense out of life. That is, for every world view, whether it be humanistic, atheistic, theistic, or whatever, there are basic assumptions and rationalizations to provide intellectual consistency and some meaning for existence. A person may unconsciously drift into his beliefs, or he may deliberately choose them to suit himself. In either case, he accepts the validity of his presuppositions on faith.

(3) For the Christian world view, the basic presuppositions are (a) that God exists, and (b) has revealed Himself in Jesus Christ; the inspired record of that revelation is the Bible. The statements of the Bible (in original text) comprise an objective data category, and these statements are to be interpreted along with other objective observable data from physical reality, within the world view. Biblical data principally treat

a different kind of reality, which we call "spiritual reality," not amenable to direct controlled observation nor scientific description. These data tell us in finite language something of the nature of the infinite God and how He interacts with His creation. As all data, these language symbols are to be interpreted consistently with other data although, because they deal with ineffable spiritual entities, they allow us to see only partly, as it were "through a glass darkly." Human experiences comprise another data category, as we by faith perceive God working in the world, and in our lives. These are highly personal subjective data, and they too are to be interpreted consistently with the other data we have, both scriptural and scientific.

(4) On the five presuppositions stated, we can build a consistent Christian world view structure. The view is both internally and externally consistent; that is, it is not self-contradictory, and it allows one to account for observed data. Even after we have extensively rationalized our faith, we should remember that it is still faith. (This is true of every view.) The Christian can satisfactorily interpret his perceptions, including data of science — from archaeology to zoology with all intermediate stops — and the rationalizing process enhances rather than detracts from the quality of his faith, for faith need not be blind, but should be reasonable. Therefore, this view can be a means of intellectual consistency for the person.

(5) In addition to intellectual consistency, and as important for the human personality, this world view provides a means of satisfying man's need of moral consistency. That is, it leads to the potential fulfillment of our spiritual natures. It achieves this by providing new motives and a new quality of life to pursue new goals. Because of our egocentricity we inherently cannot please God; even our good works are contaminated by selfishness. What our egocentric personalities

could not accomplish, God Himself does in us; when we recognize our need and turn to Him for forgiveness, He enters our lives, and remotivates us with His love. We find meaning for our lives in a love for God that is made possible by the revelation and atonement of Jesus Christ. Ultimately, our faith does not stand on the wisdom of men, but in the power of God.

VII: *A Selected Recommended Reading List*

Scattered throughout the text there are numerous footnotes containing references to books or technical articles. We will not repeat these journal references here, but only the books. In addition, we list other books and journals that may be helpful, stimulate thought along the lines suggested, or provide data to the interested student. This list is by no means exhaustive, but only illustrative. Also the viewpoints of these books vary, so one should, as always, read critically, distinguishing between raw and processed data.

A. GENERAL REFERENCES

Here we list sources of information that apply generally to the problems treated in *Faith and the Physical World.*

1. *Journals and Magazines*

American Scientist, the quarterly journal of the Sigma Xi, a scientific research honorary society, contains many well-written scientific survey articles and philosophical discussions.

Christianity Today, an evangelical Christian biweekly magazine with articles on theological, philosophical, pastoral, and other topics of varied interest. Edited by Dr. Carl F. H. Henry. A serious Christian student should at least scan every issue for articles of interest.

Eternity, an evangelical monthly, with articles of more interest to lay people, generally more introductory and more simply written.

His, the monthly magazine of Inter-Varsity Christian Fellowship, with imaginative, well-written, and relevant articles on a wide variety of topics of interest to college students. Every serious Christian should read *His* regularly.

Nature, the British equivalent of *Science,* a weekly journal with articles and research reports on a wide variety of scientific and philosophical topics. Recommended for regular perusal.

Science, the weekly journal of the American Association for the Advancement of Science, with news, comment, book reviews, survey or tutorial articles, and research reports on a wide variety of topics, heavy on the biological, chemical, and geological sciences; as can be seen from the footnotes in this book, there is a lot of data given in this journal that might be of interest to a Christian.

Scientific American, published monthly, with a wide variety of subject matter, articles by competent scientists, well-written for laymen or scientists in other fields.

The Christian Graduate, the magazine of the British Inter-Varsity Fellowship, written on a somewhat more intellectual level than *His,* but well-written and relevant for college students or graduates. Recommended reading.

2. *Books.*

Baillie, John, *Natural Science and the Spiritual Life,* lectures, British Association for Advancement of Science, 1951; published by Charles Scribner's Sons, New York, 1952; a thoroughly evangelical Christian viewpoint discussing (very briefly) the "otherness" of spiritual realities.

Burtt, Edwin A., *Man Seeks the Divine — A Study in the History and Comparison of Religions,* Harper and Row, New York, 1964 (2nd Ed.); a scholarly analysis of the philosophy of religions, interpreting data within a more or less nonreligious viewpoint.

Carnell, Edward J., *An Introduction to Christian Apologetics,* Wm. B. Eerdmans Pub. Co., Grand Rapids, 1948; a masterfully organized and stated "philosophical defense" of the Biblical Christian view. Highly recommended, as are other works of Carnell; they are theological rather than scientific in approach.

Carnell, E. J., *A Philosophy of the Christian Religion,* Wm. B. Eerdmans Pub. Co., Grand Rapids, 1952.

Clark, G. H., *A Christian View of Men and Things,* Wm. B. Eerdmans Pub. Co., Grand Rapids, 1952; and *The Philosophy of Science and Belief in God,* Craig Press, 1964; Presbyterian and Reformed Pub. (1960); both of these books of Dr. Gordon Clark present a historic, Biblical viewpoint of the theologian by which data are interpreted.

Clark, R. E. D., *Scientific Rationalism and the Christian Faith,* Inter-Varsity Press, Chicago, 1945; a short, scholarly, and evangelical treatment of Huxley's and Haldane's naturalistic views, and how they arrived at them even more irrationally than most others arrive at their world views.

Hammond, T. C., *Reasoning Faith,* Inter-Varsity Fellowship, London, 1943; a philosophical defense of the Christian view, with many topics worth careful study.

Henry, Carl F. H., *Remaking the Modern Mind*, Wm. B. Eerdmans Pub. Co., Grand Rapids, 1948; an analysis of contemporary trends in philosophy, seen from within the Christian world view, and a strong apologetic for that view.

Holmes, A. F., *Christianity and Philosophy*, Inter-Varsity Press, Chicago, 1960; an introductory and simplified account of the relationships between reason and revelation.

Lewis, C. S., *Mere Christianity*, Macmillan Co., New York, 1952 (Paperback, 1960); the combination of *The Case for Christianity, Christian Behaviour,* and *Beyond Personality* into one volume; C. S. Lewis in his inimitable and penetrating style expounds the Christian view on a variety of topics. He states simply many arguments the rest of us seem to have to state abstrusely. This book is a recommended starting point for a consideration of the good sense it makes to be a Christian.

Lewis, C. S., *Miracles — A Preliminary Study*, Macmillan Co., New York, 1947; a characteristically well-written analysis of naturalism and supernaturalism, background for acceptance of the possibility that God would intervene in nature, and did — in the coming of Christ. Recommended for a serious student or a Christian troubled by doubts.

Machen, J. G., *The Origin of Paul's Religion*, Wm. B. Eerdmans Pub. Co., Grand Rapids, 1922; a scholarly treatise that gives the evidence for the unity of viewpoint of Jesus and Paul. Highly recommended for a serious student of the New Testament.

Machen, J. Gresham, *What is Faith?*, Wm. B. Eerdmans Pub. Co., Grand Rapids, 1946 (Paperback, 1962);

a theologian's view, treating the nature of Christian faith, with excellent discussions of a number of topics treated in this book, including the value and limits of human reasoning in the approach to God, and how God interacts with the believer. Highly recommended reading.

Micklem, N., *Faith and Reason*, Gerald Duckworth & Co., Ltd., London, 1963.

Packer, J. I., *Fundamentalism and the Word of God*, Wm. B. Eerdmans Pub. Co., Grand Rapids, 1958; a top-notch analysis of the "neo-orthodox" and liberal trends in contemporary Christian circles, that clearly and reasonably states the Biblical "evangelical" view. Highly recommended reading for a serious student. It treats many subjects we have only indicated in this book.

Pollard, William G., *Chance and Providence — God's Action in a World Governed by Scientific Law*, Charles Scribner's Sons, New York, 1958; a discussion that reconciles, for Dr. Pollard at least, the Biblical notions of providence (God's action) with modern quantum mechanical (statistical) notions of causality. He takes a Christian view on this subject and one worth considering as a part of a larger *Weltanschauung*.

Ramm, Bernard, *The Christian View of Science and Scripture*, Wm. B. Eerdmans Pub. Co., Grand Rapids, 1955; one of the best books on the subject, and highly recommended for every serious student, although one would not agree with everything written there any more than in any other book. Ramm marshalls the philosophical and theological arguments well, and presents and interprets much data from the sciences. He takes effective issue with the obscurantist hyper-orthodox. Among other things, he has an extensive bibliography.

Short, A. Rendle, *Modern Discovery and the Bible*, Inter-Varsity Fellowship, London, 1952 (3rd Ed.); an excellent treatment of archaeological and other scientific data along with some Christian philosophy of science.

Van der Ziel, A., *Natural Sciences and the Christian Message*, Denison Publishers, Minneapolis, 1964; takes the position that the natural sciences and the Christian message are disparate so that there is no common ground, hence no disagreement. Perhaps controversial but worth reading to get this scientist's viewpoint.

B. BOOKS ON GENERAL SCIENTIFIC METHODS AND THE PHILOSOPHY OF PHYSICAL SCIENCE, RELATIVITY, AND QUANTUM PHYSICS

Barnett, Lincoln, *The Universe and Dr. Einstein*, Wm. Sloane Assoc. Publishers, New York, 1957; an elementary, nonmathematical, popular, almost newspaperish account of relativity, of use to the reader who is unfamiliar with the notions.

Boehme, George, and the Editors of *Fortune, The New World of Math*, Dial Press (Apollo Editions A-47), 1959; a well-written introductory account of modern mathematical notions.

D'Abro, A., *The Rise of the New Physics*, Dover Books, New York, 1951 (Reprint of *The Decline of Mechanism*, 1939); an interesting account of the reasons behind the statistical descriptions of modern physics.

Dubos, René, *Dreams of Reason: Science and Utopias*, Columbia Univ. Press, 1961; a recognition of the need for man to have some spiritual understanding because of the limitations of science, by a leading biologist.

Eddington, Sir Arthur, *The Nature of the Physical World*, Macmillan Co., New York, 1929; an introductory account — an early classic in the subject of modern physics, with some very sensible remarks about its limitations and about both the natural and the supernatural spheres of reality.

Einstein, A. and Infield L., *The Evolution of Physics — The Growth of Ideas from Early Concepts to Relativity and Quanta*, Simon and Schuster, Inc., 1938; an excellent nonmathematical treatment by two masters.

Gamow, George, *One, Two, Three, . . . Infinity*, A Mentor Book, # MD 297, The New American Library, New York, 1960; a popular explanation of a variety of facts of cosmological interest, including a presentation of the expanding universe (bang) theory.

Hadamard, Jacques, *The Psychology of Invention in the Mathematical Field*, Princeton Univ. Press, 1949; an interesting discussion of the role of intuition in logic, with many fascinating examples.

Hoyle, Fred, *The Nature of the Universe*, A Mentor Book, #M 125, The New American Library, New York, 1950; an introductory, popular account of the continuous creation theory of cosmology, with some philosophical extrapolation.

Kline, Morris, *Mathematics in Western Culture*, Oxford Univ. Press, New York, 1953; a fine discussion of the influences of mathematics in arts, literature, the sciences, and in philosophy. This is recommended reading for any educated person and, although the naturalist viewpoint occasionally slips through, much interesting information is given.

Lindsay, R. B. and Margenau, Henry, *The Foundations of Physics*, John Wiley & Sons, Inc., New York, 1936; a treatise on classical and modern physics, with necessary mathematics, and with considerable well-expressed insight into the nature of scientific methods.

Margenau, Henry, *The Nature of Physical Reality — A Philosophy of Modern Physics*, McGraw-Hill Book Co.,

Inc., New York, 1950; an excellent but technical presentation of scientific methods and the subject matter of science. The view is neither theistic nor atheistic, as Professor Margenau recognizes the limitations of science.

Nagel, E. and Newman, J. R., *Gödel's Proof*, New York Univ. Press, 1958; about as readable account of this subject as could be given.

Neurath, Otto, Carnap, Rudolf, and Morris, C. W., Editors, *International Encyclopedia of Unified Science*, Vol. 1, Univ. of Chicago Press, 1955; an analytic, positivist apologetic, presenting that philosophical view of science. This two-part book is recommended principally as a reference for scientific methodology, but its strong and occasionally obvious viewpoint should be taken into account.

Öpik, Ernst J., *The Oscillating Universe*, A Mentor Book, # MD 289, The New American Library, New York, 1960; an introductory popular account of the currently most acceptable cosmological theory, with some philosophical extrapolation.

Peierls, R. E., *The Laws of Nature*, Charles Scribner's Sons, New York, 1956; a somewhat more modern (than Eddington) but still elementary account of physics.

Polya, G., *Mathematics and Plausible Reasoning;* Volume I, *Induction and Analogy in Mathematics*; Volume II, *Patterns of Plausible Inference*, Princeton Univ. Press, 1954; a readable textbook on the subject of reasoning, highly recommended to a serious student of science.

Tarski, Alfred, *Introduction to Logic and to the Methodology of Deductive Sciences*, Oxford Univ. Press, New York, 1946 (2nd Ed.); a comprehensive introductory text on symbolic, sentential, and mathematical logic.

von Weizsäcker, C. F., *The World View of Physics*, Univ. of Chicago Press, 1952; a somewhat heavy but worth-the-effort discussion by a leading physicist, who understands the limitations of science and sees the need for the extrascientific approaches to meaning in life.

Wilder, Raymond L., *Introduction to the Foundations of Mathematics*, John Wiley & Sons, New York, 1952; a technical account of modern mathematics from a fundamental viewpoint.

C. BOOKS ON THE MANIFOLD NATURE OF MAN AND HUMAN (BIOLOGICAL AND BEHAVIORAL) SCIENCES

Anfinson, Christian B., *The Molecular Basis of Evolution*, John Wiley & Sons, New York, 1959; a technical account of the biochemistry data that is consistent with the evolutionary hypothesis.

Borek, Ernest, *The Code of Life*, Columbia Univ. Press, New York, 1965; a modern, readable, and accurate account of the biochemical basis of genetics.

Clark, W. Le Gros, *Fossil Evidence for Human Evolution*, Univ. of Chicago Press, 1964 (2nd Ed.); a review of data and interpretations thereof on the subject.

Dobzhansky, Theodosius, *Mankind Evolving*, Yale Univ. Press, New Haven, 1962; a presentation of a point of view, with considerable admixed data, on the interdependence of cultural and biological factors in evolution.

Inter-Varsity Fellowship, *A Christian Approach to Psychological Medicine*, Inter-Varsity Fellowship, London, 1957; an excellent monograph outlining the relationship of psychological science to Christian belief.

James, William, *The Varieties of Religious Experience, A Study in Human Nature*, The Modern Library, New York, 1902; a classic work on the subject.

Jung, C. G., *Modern Man in Search of a Soul*, Harcourt, Brace Co., New York, 1933 (1955-reprint); a recommended classic.

Kalmus, H., *Genetics*, A Pelican Book, #A-179, Penguin Books, Harmondsworth, 1945; an introductory survey of the field.

Lewis, C. S., *The Abolition of Man*, Macmillan Co., New York, 1947; an interesting discussion on the trends in modern education and the basic human need for extra-scientific or suprarational meaning. Recommended.

McKenzie, J. G., *Nervous Disorders and Religion*, Geo. Allen and Unwin, Ltd., London, 1951; a highly recommended study of the drives of basic human nature and the ways religious experience can either enhance or hinder personality integration.

McKenzie, J. G., *Psychology, Psychotherapy, and Evangelicalism*, Geo. Allen and Unwin, Ltd., London, 1940; a highly recommended work on the psychological nature of Christian experience.

Mottram, V. H., *The Physical Basis of Personality*, A Pelican Book, #A-139, Penguin Books, Harmondsworth, 1944; an introductory but clear account of the hereditary factors in human personality.

Mowrer, Orral H., *The Crisis in Psychiatry and Religion*, Van Nostrand, Princeton Univ. Press, 1961; an account of the changing attitudes on both sides of the old argument between psychiatric and religious dogmatists.

Sluckin, W., *Minds and Machines*, A Pelican Book, #A-308, Penguin Books, Harmondsworth, 1954; a useful book for background information on computers and the concepts of the human mind.

Tyrell, G. N. M., *The Personality of Man*, A Pelican Book, #A-165, Penguin Books, Harmondsworth, 1945; a non-technical and interesting discussion of psychical research and speculations on its relation to the nature of man.

White, Ernest, *Christian Life and the Unconscious*, Harper and Row, New York, 1955; a highly recommended study of Christian experience from a psychiatrist's point of view.

Wright, J. Stafford, *Man in the Process of Time*, Wm. B. Eerdmans Pub. Co., Grand Rapids, 1955; a somewhat "far out" book, but interesting and certainly far-ranging in scope of subject matter, from telepathy to occultism to aesthetics to a philosophy of science.

D. BOOKS ON BIBLICAL PROBLEMS, CRITICISM, ARCHAEOLOGY, AND HISTORY

Aalders, G. C., *The Problem of the Book of Jonah*, Tyndale Press, London, 1948; another of the monographs that deals with a specific problem, recommended for any with the problem.

Albright, W. F., *The Archaeology of Palestine*, Pelican Book, #A-199, Harmondsworth, 1954 (3rd Rev.); an excellent authoritative survey with lots of raw data.

Albright, W. F., *From the Stone Age to Christianity — Monotheism and the Historical Process*, Johns Hopkins Univ. Press, Baltimore, 1957 (2nd Ed.); also an authoritative book full of both raw and interpreted data, but generally sympathetic to the Christian view.

Barton, George A., *Archaeology and the Bible*, American Sunday School Union, Philadelphia, 1937 (7th Ed.); still one of the best and most complete (with data up to 1937) accounts of the subject, with many photographs and translations of ancient literatures. Highly recommended reading as a means of getting at some raw data of archaeology.

Broomall, Wick, *Biblical Criticism*, Zondervan Pub. Co., Grand Rapids, 1957; an introductory but technically sound accounting of critical methods as used by Biblical scholars, with discussions of some topics we have only mentioned in this book. Highly recommended for a serious student.

Bruce, F. F., *The New Testament Documents: Are They Reliable?*, Wm. B. Eerdmans Pub. Co., Grand Rapids, 1960 (5th Ed.); an excellent discussion of the subject, recommended for the serious student.

Bruce, F. F., *The Teacher of Righteousness in the Qumran Texts*, Tyndale Press, London, 1956; a pamphlet highly recommended to the serious student.

Finegan, Jack, *Light from the Ancient Past*, Princeton Univ. Press, 1959 (2nd Ed.); a well-written presentation of archaeological information, much of which is related to Biblical history.

Frazer, Sir J. G., *The Golden Bough,* Macmillan Co., New York, 1958 (6th printing); a classic book on primitive culture, with much data given and interpreted within a naturalistic world view. Needs critical reading to glean the data, but worth it.

Keller, Werner, *The Bible as History*, Wm. Morrow and Co., New York, 1964; an excellent treatise in interesting narrative style relating Biblical history to archaeological data. Highly recommended.

LaSor, William S., *Dead Sea Scrolls and the Christian Faith*, Moody Press, Chicago, 1962 (revision of *Amazing Dead Sea Scrolls,* 1956); one of the most readable accounts of the Qumran literature data and their relationship to the Christian origins. Highly recommended.

Libby, Willard F., *Radiocarbon Dating*, Univ. of Chicago Press, 1955 (2nd Ed.); a description of the C-14 technique by the man who developed it originally.

Manley, G. T., Editor, *The New Bible Handbook*, Inter-Varsity Fellowship, London, 1950 (3rd Ed.); an excellent general accounting of textual and critical problems, followed by synopses and discussions of Biblical content.

Mansoor, Menahen, *The Dead Sea Scrolls,* Wm. B. Eerdmans Pub. Co., Grand Rapids, 1964; a college text and study guide, for a specialist who wants to get the technical data.

Martin, W. J., *Stylistic Criteria and the Analysis of the Pentateuch,* Tyndale Press, London, 1955; another not-too-technical pamphlet recommended for study.

Oakley, Kenneth, *Frameworks for Dating Fossil Man,* Aldine Pub. Co., Chicago, 1964; a discussion of dating techniques, using geological, cultural, and radiation methods.

Ramm, Bernard, *Protestant Christian Evidences,* Moody Press, Chicago, 1959; a discussion of evidences, prophecy, miracles, and other related subjects, presented in a scholarly theologian's way within the Christian world view. A recommended source book.

Robertson, A. T., *Introduction to the Textual Criticism of the New Testament,* Broadman Press, Nashville, 1925; a technical but introductory account of New Testament manuscripts, versions, readings, and critical methods.

Runia, Klaas, *I Believe in God . . .* , Inter-Varsity Press, Chicago, 1963; a discussion of church creeds that spills over into the subject of inspiration, criticism, and "the new liberalism" of Bultmann, Tillich, et al. Well worth reading.

Schmidt, W., *The Origin and Growth of Religion — Facts and Theories,* H. J. Rose, trans., Methuen & Co., London, 1935; a presentation of Schmidt's data on monotheism in primitive societies, well worth reading, since it gives data most anthropologists (for philosophical reasons) do not account for.

Schmidt, W., *Primitive Revelation,* J. J. Baierl, trans., B. Herder Book Co., London, 1939; also presenting the primitive monotheism theory. Hard to find, but highly recommended.

Swanson, Guy E., *The Birth of the Gods,* Univ. of Mich. Press, Ann Arbor, 1960; a more modern accounting for anthropological data, within a naturalistic world view. The tendency is to conclude that his philosophical view is correct because the author can account for data, neglecting the fact that other views also allow for consistent interpretation of the same data. Recommended for a specialist who can give it the necessary critical reading.

Unger, Merrill F., *Archaeology of the Old Testament,* 1962, *Archaeology of the New Testament,* Zondervan Pub. Co., Grand Rapids, 1954.

Wenham, J. W., *Our Lord's View of the Old Testament,* Tyndale Press, London, 1953; a recommended monograph for a discussion of Old Testament inspiration.

Wright, G. E., Editor, *The Bible and the Ancient Near East — Essays in Honor of W. F. Albright,* A Doubleday Anchor Book, A-431, Garden City, N. Y., 1965; a set of essays by authorities in the field, with a lot of data as well as interpretation and philosophy. Worth some critical study,

Wright, G. E., and Freeman, D. N., Editors, *The Biblical Archaeologist Reader,* Doubleday Anchor Books, A-250, Garden City, N. Y., 1961; a collection of essays and articles from the *Biblical Archaeologist,* the journal of the American Schools of Oriental Research, presenting much data, both raw and interpreted within a variety of world views. Worth critical study.

Young, Edward J., *An Introduction to the Old Testament,* Wm. B. Eerdmans Pub. Co., Grand Rapids, 1960 (Rev. Ed.); a detailed and comprehensive analysis of Old Testament textual and critical problems. Recommended for study by a serious student of the faith.

E. BOOKS NOT OBVIOUSLY CLASSIFIABLE IN A-D ABOVE

Bayly, Joseph, *The Gospel Blimp*, Windward Press, Havertown, Penn., 1960; an amusing but provocative parable of modern fundamentalism's misguided attempts to share its views with a spiritually hungry world. Well worth reading.

Bingham, Geoffry C., *Liberating Love*, M.I.K. Press, Lahore, Pakistan, 1957; a guide to experiencing the love of God in the Christian life; unfortunately not (as far as is known) published nor widely available in the U. S.

Du Noüy, Lecompte, *Road to Reason*, Longmans, Green, and Co., New York, 1949; a philosophy of science and life that argues for the necessity of spiritual realities to provide meaning to the data of science.

Einstein, Albert, *Out of My Later Years*, Philosophical Library, New York, 1950; a collection of essays on various topics, well worth reading for an understanding of how a great man thinks.

Jewett, Paul K., *Emil Brunner, An Introduction to the Man and His Thought*, Inter-Varsity Press, Chicago, 1961; an interesting elementary analysis of the strengths and weaknesses of the neo-orthodox position.

Kilby, Clyde S., *Christianity and Aesthetics*, Inter-Varsity Press, Chicago, 1961; some insights into the indicated relationship.

Lewis, C. S., *The Pilgrim's Regress* (1943), Wm. B. Eerdmans Pub. Co., Grand Rapids; *The Problem of Pain* (1940), and *The Four Loves* (1960), Geoffrey Bles Pub., London. All highly recommended reading.

Rehwinkel, A., *The Flood*, Concordia, 1951; a discussion of catastrophism, which is a view not supported by the majority of geological data, but which is invoked to support a specific Biblical interpretation. Worth reading to see how many dogmatic Christians rationalize views on science.

Riegel, David, *Creation or Evolution,* Concordia, 1962; a book that sets up the alternatives of its title as though there were no middle ground, but giving some data to be accounted for. Worth reading to see how many dogmatic Christians rationalize their views on science.

Schroedinger, E., *What is Life?,* Macmillan Co., New York, 1946; a famous physicist's approach to molecular biology, with some philosophical discussion.

Shapley, Harlow, Editor, *A Treasury of Science,* Harper & Row (1958) (4th Ed.); a panorama of science and philosophy essays, a very interesting sampler.

Standen, Anthony, *Science is a Sacred Cow,* Dutton Co., New York, 1950; a somewhat tongue-in-cheek analysis of "scientism" as it is practiced by modern Americans.

St. Augustine, *Confessions,* The Modern Library, New York, 1945.

Toynbee, Arnold, *Civilization on Trial,* Oxford Univ. Press, New York, 1948; an analysis of the times in which we live.

Toynbee, Arnold, *Reconsiderations — A Study of History,* Volume XII, Oxford Univ. Press, New York, 1961; a comprehensive reanalysis of Toynbee's earlier works in the study of history, recommended for a serious student.

Trueblood, Elton, *Foundations for Reconstruction,* Harper & Row, New York, 1946; a sequel to *Predicament,* a modern reinterpretation of the Ten Commandments.

Trueblood, Elton, *The Predicament of Modern Man,* Harper & Row, New York, 1944; recommended reading for an analysis of the times.

Velikovsky, Immanuel, *Worlds in Collision*, Macmillan Co., New York, 1950; a controversial book on the theory that cosmic cataclysms within the span of recorded history are responsible for many legends and other data of anthropology and history. Few astronomers (or other scientists) accept these views; he presents some data which may usually be accounted for by more conventional theories. It seems risky to base astronomical theories so heavily on primitive cultural records.

Wiener, Norbert, *The Human Use of Human Beings, Cybernetics and Society*, Houghton, Mifflin Co., Boston, 1950; a somewhat humanistic approach to ethics, but one that shows the moral neutrality and vast potential of technology, and the need for men who will choose to use technology for good rather than evil.

Index of Subjects

Index of Authors

209

Index of Biblical References
and Quotations

(Note: This index differs from the usual index of Scripture in that the name of the Bible book has been omitted from the text. Thus on page 14 there is no citation of I Timothy 6:20 but simply a quotation from this passage.)

211

Page	Reference	Key Thought
99	II Corinthians 5:14	love of Christ directs us
99n.	Jeremiah 2:13;	
	Romans 1:25	substitutes for God
99	Galatians 5:6	faith operates by love
99	Philippians 2:13	God energizes our lives
99	John 10:10	abundant living
100	John 7:17	willingness
101	I John 5:20	given us understanding to know
101	Ephesians 6:16	shield of faith
102	Psalm 85:10	righteousness and truth
102	Jeremiah 2:13	dry wells
102	John 7:37-39	living waters
103	John 8:30-36	slaves to sin
103	Matthew 22:37-40	love the Lord fully
107	II Kings 18:13-19:37	siege of Jerusalem
109	I Corinthians 10:1-12	Old Testament illustrates New
110	Micah 6:8	a purpose of revelation
113	II Corinthians 5:7	walk by faith
113	Deuteronomy 3:11;	
	Joshua 17:16	early mentions of iron
114	Genesis 4:22	first mention of copper
114	Daniel 5:29	Daniel third in kingdom
115	Daniel 2:28-45;	
	11:31-33	prophecies
116	Genesis 13:12-13;	
	19:1-30	Sodom and Gomorrah
119n.	Psalm 104:19-20	compare with Ikhnaton's hymn
122	Hebrews 1:1-3	God has spoken
122	Colossians 2:9	God dwells in Christ
122	John 14:9-10	see Christ, see God
122	II Timothy 3:16-17	Scripture is inspired
124	Romans 15:4	Scriptures for later learning
124	II Peter 1:20	prophets misunderstood
134	Genesis 1:1; John 1:1	beginnings
134	Revelation 21:6	Alpha and Omega
135	Hebrews 11:3	understand by faith
139	Genesis 1:6-20	creation narratives
144	Genesis 1:20-25	creation narratives
146	Genesis 1:26-7; 2:7-9	creation of man
147n.	Genesis 2:10-14	four rivers
147	Genesis 2:18-25	creation of Eve
149	John 4:24	spiritual nature of God
150	Genesis 1:31	creation was good
151	Genesis 4-11	prehistory before Abram
152	Genesis 4:17, 26;	
	6:2, 8; 10:1-32	incidents in Seth's line
152	Ephesians 2:8-10	grace and faith

Page	Reference	Key Thought
153	Genesis 11:1-10	Babel tower incident
154	Genesis 6-9	flood narrative
154	Matthew 24:36-44	example of Noah
155	Romans 1:20-32	degeneration of race
157	Genesis 4:20	Jabal
159	II Corinthians 7:10	repentance
160	Hebrews 3:8	"harden not your heart"
161	Romans 12:3	humility
161	I Corinthians 1:18-30	God's wisdom surpasses
162	I Corinthians 1:24	Christ, the wisdom of God
163	Philippians 3:7-9	abdicate self-righteousness
163	I Samuel 16:7	God looks at hearts
164n.	I Corinthians 8, 12; Romans 14	God deals individually
164	II Corinthians 11:3	simplicity in Christ
164	Galatians 5:4	falling from grace
164	I Timothy 6:17	enjoyment of life
165	II Corinthians 5:7	walk by faith
165	Colossians 2:20-23	self-devised ethics
165	Galatians 5:1, 4, 5, 13	legalism vs. freedom
166	II Corinthians 4:17	liberty in Spirit
166	Ephesians 2:8-9	not works, but grace saves
167	Romans 11:5-6	disjointedness of works and grace
167	I Corinthians 1:23	foolishness of cross
167	Acts 20:24	gospel of grace
167	Galatians 5:22-23	fruit of Spirit
167	Hebrews 12:6-11	chastens as sons
167	Galatians 5:16-17	flesh vs. Spirit
168	II Chronicles 20:15	battle is God's
168	John 16:33	cheer up
168	Hebrews 12:14	holiness
168	I John 5:4-5	victory
169	Hebrews 8:10-12	a new desire to do good
169	II Corinthians 5:14	love of Christ constrains
169	I Corinthians 6:19-20	not our own, glorify God
169	Colossians 4:1-4	object of affection above
169	John 14:20	indwelling of God
169	I John 1:5-9	fellowship, confession, forgiveness
170	II Peter 1:3	spiritual resources
171n.	John 10:10; 17:3	life eternal and abundant
173	I John 2:10	misbehavior causes stumbling
176	I Corinthians 2:16	mind of Christ
178	Philippians 3:11-14	press on to high calling
180	I Corinthians 13:12	through translucent glass
181	Romans 8:3-4	human inadequacy — God's accomplishment
181	I Corinthians 2:5	faith rests on God's power